TICK-TOCK

TICK-TOCK

BY PROFESSOR A. M. LOW

*With Pen Drawings
by Amy Low*

ROBERT M. McBRIDE & COMPANY
NEW YORK

J
500
L

AMERICAN BOOK—STRATFORD PRESS, INC., NEW YORK

DEDICATED
TO
"TEDDY" LOW

Contents

Illustrations

TICK-TOCK

*All the characters in this book
are true*

Introduction

But there is no need to read it

I USED to worry when I saw trees, spiders, dormice, flies, flowers and the sun; all shutting up their lives in winter-time. . . . Until I noticed someone going to sleep in a railway carriage. Then I thought how frightened I would be if I had never seen sleep before; for I might wonder if people were going away altogether.

You say: "Don't be silly, they are resting." And then I began to wonder when flies rested and I thought how tired trees must be after a windy day. They need rest just as much as we do.

So winter helps them. While we sleep all

kinds of things happen but we always wake up feeling "un-tired". It is good to sleep. But remember that sleep is a busy time inside and if you could look out of the window on a cold, wet day with eyes so strong that you could see bluebottles a mile away you would be surprised because no one else could see them except *you*. If you woke up and everything in the world had grown ten times larger—what would you think? Nothing at all, because the difference in size between you and a cat would still be the same. Do you see what I mean? That could be called relativity. A silly word for so simple a thing.

Nature works very hard. Flowers turn to the sun, the convolvulus struggles and succeeds in penetrating concrete to reach the sun. The snail moves slowly compared to the speed of a butterfly's flight, but both go fast in their own minds. The fly buzzing round a room thinks it is in a vast undiscovered universe. It is all relative.

You, when you dream, can live through years in a second. Never let time frighten you, for it is really all there before you, the past, the present and the future.

The golden thread running through everything is the continuity of life. Nothing dies, nothing is lost, not even the smallest fragment. Think rightly and clearly for that is what matters most. And because you think a thing is small and insignificant—to *you*—do not despise it. In nature's scheme everything has a place, and is all very important indeed.

This book begins in winter because so many things you can see are asleep and so many that you cannot see are wide awake.

The Beginning

If nothing ever happened,
And there were no things to place,
There'd be no need for any time,
Or use for any space.
In awful global nothingness
The molecules would play,
Last week would be to-morrow,
And yesterday to-day!

"WE'RE lost, Twinks!"

Bill scratched his tousled hair, nearly fell off the bank top, and all at once looked down at his sister who sat on a large boulder by the roadside.

"Well, if we are lost it doesn't matter. Someone'll come along some time, and it's far too hot to walk any more."

Twinks shut her eyes and tried to fan herself with a dock leaf.

Bill looked about him. As far as his eyes could see there spread out north, south, east, and west, vast seas of rolling green downland threaded by silver-grey ribbon of dusty road. Not a soul was in sight. Only against the sky's brilliant blue a hawk hovered.

"I wonder what the time is?"

Bill scrambled down from the bank to the road. Twinks opened a lazy eye to blink at him.

"How you do fuss," she complained. "There's plenty of time."

"Yes, there's always plenty of time if you know where to look for it!" said a voice behind them.

Twinks and Bill turned round sharply. It was really *quite* unbelievable, but out of nowhere had appeared a queer little man. He was rosy-cheeked, tubby as to his figure, and with a smiling face. His broad-

[17]

OVER THE DOWNS

*Rabbits, hedgehogs, birds, butterflies, beetles and nearly every-
thing else have their homes in the hedges or banks, all the
year round*

brimmed hat, his suit and canvas shoes
were of spotless white, and he carried an
enormous red and blue umbrella.

"Excuse me," he said, bowing first to

Twinks and then to Bill. "My name is Pobblethwaite, Tempus Pobblethwaite at your service. If you want time I think I can help you, for as I remarked before, there's always plenty of time!"

As he said this he stumped with his umbrella on the ground two or three times to emphasize his words.

Twinks got up from her boulder. "Please," she said, "we've lost our way and we don't know what the right time is. We're staying at Drummetts Mill. Can you help us?"

Bill chimed in: "And we don't want to be late for tea."

Mr. Tempus Pobblethwaite took out a red bandana handkerchief from one of his capacious pockets and mopped his face.

"I can tell you any time you like," he replied solemnly in the manner of a bishop delivering a sermon, "if you tell me what sort of time you want. Slow like the plants, or fast like some of my friends the insects. Past, present, or future. This year, next year, sometime, anything but never. But perhaps the best plan will be for you to come into my shop and choose your own."

Then, slowly he waved his handkerchief in front of him.

For once in their lives Twinks and Bill were speechless. Where but a moment before had been dusty road and steep banks, now stood a neat little house, blue-shuttered, red-tiled. Over its doorway hung a signboard bearing the words:

TEMPUS POBBLETHWAITE
Keeper of the King's Time

"It's perfectly right," remarked Mr. Pobblethwaite. He actually seemed to be a little cross at their astonishment. "Come in and I'll show you all the time in the world." And he lifted the latch of the door and led the way inside.

The shop was very dark as Twinks and Bill stepped in rather gingerly. All around them they heard the ticking of clocks.

Tick—tock—tick—tock

went some quite steadily.

Tickety—tockety—tickety—tockety

went others very fast.

Tick—ticktocktick—tocketyticktickety

rushed others as if in desperate hurry to catch up.

"Just a moment," Mr. Pobblethwaite said, "I'll get a light. Puss, Puss, Puss, where is that dratted cat?"

Twinks felt something soft brush against her legs in the dark, and suddenly up went a shower of sparks and they saw Mr. Pobblethwaite stooping down and stroking the fur of a huge grey Persian cat.

"Far better than matches, aren't you, Electra?" he murmured, lighting a paper spill from the sparks and then putting the flame to two candles that stood on a shelf.

"That's a jolly good idea, isn't it, Bill?"

Twinks remarked. "Fancy keeping a cat just to save matches. I wonder why no one thought of it before."

"I can show you another good time-saving plan," their host answered as he drew out of his pocket a small tin box. Inside this were three funny little beetles that gave off a sort of phosphorescent glow. "My glow-worms," said Mr. Pobblethwaite, "they do instead of a lantern on dark nights. Very useful—I could not do without them," and he put the box back in his coat with an air of pride. He then proceeded to light a number of candles and his two visitors could see the queer room in which they were standing.

In every nook and corner, hanging on the walls, standing on tables and shelves, and even on the floor, were clocks. Big, little and medium-sized ones. Grandfather and grandmother clocks, cuckoo clocks, alarm clocks—in fact every kind of clock imaginable, and all tick-tocking away as if for dear life.

"Do you sell clocks?" Bill asked curiously.

"Bless the boy, of course not, only time," replied Mr. Pobblethwaite laughing.

Twinks was mystified. "How can you sell time? It's nothing you can touch or feel, and who buys it anyway?"

"My dear young friend," Mr. Pobblethwaite scratched his chin thoughtfully as though at a loss for words.

"Everyone buys time," he went on, "without time we should be in a very bad way. There would be no time to enjoy the sun, or the rain, no time to sleep, no time to wake, no time for eggs to hatch, buds to open or seeds to grow." He shook his head vigorously at such a terrible thought.

Bill looked puzzled. "I've often wondered why nice time goes so quickly and bad times so slowly," he said.

"Yes," put in Twinks, "like the way holidays fly and school seems to go on for ever. And," she put in before Mr. Pobblethwaite could reply, "do tell us, why do you keep the King's Time, can't he look after it himself?"

Over Mr. Pobblethwaite's chubby face spread a reverential look.

"The King's Time, why the King's Time is *most* important. When His Majesty is pressed for time all he has to do is to send the Lord Most High Chamberlain down to me and I then arrange for him to have all the time he wants. This is the King's Time."

As he spoke the last few words His Majesty's Time Keeper walked over to a fine grandfather clock that stood in a corner of the shop surmounted by a carved crown. It ticked away steadily "tick-tock tick-tock", in perfect rhythm.

"Now," said Mr. Pobblethwaite as the two peered upwards at the great shining dial, "suppose His Majesty has so many matters of state to attend to that he is short of time. He sends to me and I adjust the royal pendulum so." He opened the door of the clock and disclosed two hanging weights and a swinging pendulum. Delicately he moved a small circular weight on the end of the pendulum. "The Royal Time now goes slower, thus giving His Majesty plenty of time to carry out all his work in perfect comfort. Listen," and he held up his hand.

The Royal time-piece was still ticking but it went tick—tock—tick—tock, so slowly that you could count ten between the tick-tocks.

Bill blinked his eyes, cocked his head to listen again to the clock. Then he said: "Well, I never knew you could play tricks with time like that."

Twinks chimed in : "Does it really mean that time is just the space to do things in between the ticks of a clock?"

On Mr. Pobblethwaite's face a broad grin developed. He seemed to take an almost impish delight in mystifying his visitors.

"Perhaps you could call it that," he answered, "for if there was no time, everything that happened would be squashed together into one event. It just needs a little re-arrangement, and that is *my* business as the Royal Time Keeper." His ample chest positively swelled with pride as he spoke.

"Look here," he added as he saw the complete bewilderment on the faces of his audience. "If you would care to accompany me on my rounds I will try to show how time works."

Twinks clapped her hands delightedly. But the more thoughtful Bill seemed dubious. "You know we promised not to be late for tea," he told her.

"Ha, ha, ha," laughed Mr. Pobblethwaite, and he drew their attention to an oval-faced clock which recorded that it was just 3.25 p.m.

"If you come with me I will promise to get you back here again at 3.20 p.m., so just leave it to me, will you?"

Before they could either of them say a word, Mr. Pobblethwaite had dragged

down a box from a shelf and taken out
of it two pairs of huge tortoise-shell spectacles. These he handed to Bill and Twinks,
saying gravely: "Hold them carefully,
and whatever happens, do not put them
on till I tell you to." Then, with an air of
mystery, he added: "Now; follow me."

He stepped to the shop door and flung
it wide open. Grasping their spectacles
firmly, Bill and Twinks followed him outside.

"Ooh, ooh, I say," they cried out together.

The whole scene had changed. Gone
were the greens and blues, the colours of
sky, trees and downs. There was snow
everywhere. In the air, and on the ground.
From every tree hung long glittering
icicles, over the stones and bushes lay a
coating of powdery frost.

Mr. Pobblethwaite enjoyed their astonishment.

"And you'll be quite warm," he said
meaningly.

The two suddenly looked at each other. "Why, we've got different clothes," cried Twinks.

Sure enough their summer clothes had disappeared and in place of them they were wearing thick blanket coats and high fur-trimmed boots. On their heads were fur caps, and sticking out of the coat pockets were fur gloves. Mr. Pobblethwaite was dressed in much the same way, except that his coat was scarlet with gold buttons, while theirs were of more sombre blue.

"Put on your glasses now," ordered Mr. Pobblethwaite suddenly.

With fumbling fingers Bill and Twinks obeyed, adjusting the thick side pieces under their fur caps.

Twinks was the first to speak. "Bill, oh Bill, it's marvellous," she shouted in her excitement. "Why, I can see right through the snow."

Winter

The daffodil whimpered: "Oh, why
Can't I sleep all my life till I die?"
But the Time Keeper said:
"Nothing *ever* is dead,
And you'd merely change shape by and by!"

SNOW was falling. Not very heavily, but
there were flakes in the air, and through
their new spectacles Bill and Twinks saw
that each flake was a mass of glittering
crystals cut into different shapes and
reflecting the light from a hundred smooth
surfaces.

"Why, they sparkle like the stones in
Mother's ring," said Twinks, and when
she caught one in her hand it was so bright
that she could hardly bear to look at it.

[29]

"They look like flowers, I think," Bill said, letting two or three of the flakes fall on his hand. "They're all different patterns, too; if they had stalks they would be just like flowers, wouldn't they, Mr. Pobblethwaite?"

"Yes, my boy, those snowflakes are every one of them different, and there's no artist I know who can design anything half so fine. And they're alive too, they grow and change if you give them time!" As he said this Mr. Pobblethwaite's bright eyes twinkled almost as brightly as the crystals.

"Look at the bank, Twinks." Bill forgot the snowflakes in his excitement. "Look at the bank, why, it's really a house."

Indeed, the snow-covered bank *was* a house all built up of twisted roots of trees and bushes matted together. Here and there were rough doors and odd-shaped windows, some round like a squirrel's

NATURE'S DORMITORY

Gaffer Mole hurries up the daffodils. Flowers always know the right time

nest, others square or oblong. Sometimes a sharp point of light showed up for a moment or a queer face peered out from a corner. It was a most disconcerting kind of house, but at the same time strangely exciting.

"Please, dear Mr. Pobblethwaite," begged Twinks, her blue eyes starry, "may we go and see what it's like inside?"

"Surely, surely, my dear." Mr. Pobblethwaite looked kindly down at the eager face. "It's part of my work to visit Nature's dormitories and see that the clocks are right so that none of the sleepers are late for work. Perhaps you will be able to hear more about time from them. Let us go in at once."

Suiting the action to the word, Mr. Pobblethwaite stepped up to the nearest door in the strange house and rapped sharply on it with his umbrella.

After a moment or two there came the sound of shuffling footsteps, a rattle of chains, bolts were drawn, and as the door swung open a hoarse voice asked:

"Who's that a-comin' just when folks has got to sleep?"

It was a large velvet-coated mole that spoke. A pair of huge smoked glasses perched precariously on his pink nose and he held up a horn lantern the better to see the faces of his callers.

When he saw Mr. Pobblethwaite his tone changed to one of pleasure.

"Why, 'tis the Time Keeper, it be," he wheezed, "always glad to see 'ee I be— and yer friends," he nodded to Bill and Twinks. "What can I do for 'ee?"

"Good evening, Gaffer," said Mr. Pobblethwaite genially, stepping forward.

"As it was my time for attending to the clocks I thought you would not object to my bringing two young friends of mine along with me. They are very anxious to learn what time really is. Perhaps you could help them?"

As he said this the King's Time Keeper solemnly winked one eye at Gaffer Mole as much as to say, "Did you ever hear anything so absurd?"

The mole scratched his furry chin gravely.

" 'Tis a difficult thing you've asked, Mr. Time Keeper," he grunted. "There's all sorts of time. Maybe the young folk'll let me know what time they want. Let 'em come along in and then they can see for themselves what is a-goin' on here." He threw open the door wide and beckoned them inside.

Mr. Pobblethwaite, Bill and Twinks followed their noses after Gaffer Mole. He led them along narrow winding passages and they bumped their heads against low ceilings and jutting-out walls. They passed doors on which they could just see inscriptions such as "Fish", "Frogs" and "This way to the Camouflage Room".

At last, when they thought they would never reach the end, the mole stopped in front of a door marked "Flowers and Insects".

He pushed it open. "Come in," he invited.

[34]

Eager to see what was inside, Bill and Twinks hurried over the threshold behind Mr. Pobblethwaite.

The room in which they stood was very large and it was lined from floor to ceiling with rows of little wooden bunks. At one end a huge log fire burned on an open hearth and above the fire-place hung a broad-faced eight-day clock on the dial of which were many white markings. Scuttling about the room were numbers of grey squirrels, squeaking to each other, sweeping in corners, piling leaves on the bunks and generally making themselves useful.

Mr. Pobblethwaite approached the big clock with a certain air of proprietorship, and proceeded to bring out of his coat pocket a large iron handle.

"Before I wind it up," he said, "take a good look at the clock; it tells all kinds of time, and it's the first you've seen like that, I'll be bound."

Twinks and Bill went up close to the

[35]

chimney-piece and gazed wide-eyed at the clock. Instead of the usual figures this clock had words. There were the twelve months of the year indicated by one hand, and there was another hand that pointed to another set of words such as "Cuckoo time", "Bluebell time", and "Rose time".

"What does it mean?" asked Bill. "Why should bluebells and roses have times of their own? I think this time business is jolly muddling."

Gaffer Mole, who had come up behind them, snorted scornfully.

"What do they teach 'ee at school?" he grumbled. "None of us, not even them flowers, live at the same time. Sure, if the roses and bluebells conned out together there'd be no room for 'em all. They all has to bide their turn, same as young maister. Us can't have no monkeyin' 'bout with time down here, us can't." And with that he scuffled across the room to box the ears of one of the squirrels who had dropped a bundle of leaves on the red-tiled floor.

But Bill persisted; Gaffer Mole's explanation did not satisfy his logical mind.

"But who gives them time, how do they know what their time is?" he queried.

Mr. Pobblethwaite, who was by then opening the clock case and was about to insert the handle into a hole in the face in order to wind it up, stopped for a moment to reply.

"I look after the clocks here," he told Bill, "but as for time itself, well," he hesitated a little, "time's everywhere, we're using it now. If you could see better you could see into your past time as well as into your time to come. It's all yours, all the yesterdays, to-days and to-morrows. Nothing of time disappears." Here Mr. Pobblethwaite clasped one hand to his ample chest as if he was indeed embracing time and the heavy handle fell to the floor with a crash.

"But how do the flowers know when it is time to wake up?" Twinks asked as she stooped to pick up the handle for Mr. Pobblethwaite.

The Time Keeper smiled as he again inserted the winder.

"Listen," he told her. "The clock is about to strike."

One of the hands had reached the words "First springs", and a peal of bells chimed through the big room.

At once Gaffer Mole and some of the squirrels began to set up a long ladder against one of the walls and to push its topmost rungs through a gap in the roof. There was a quick rustling in the bunks. The piles of dead leaves began to heave to and fro and were scattered as out of their warm beds clambered scores of strange little brown creatures.

Some were brown, round and fat; others slender and smooth. All wore dark cloaks wrapped about them and seemed intent on getting away somewhere as fast as they could. They all made for the ladder and began to scramble away out of sight through the hole in the roof.

Twinks put out a hand as one little figure sped past her.

"Who are you, what's your name?" she asked.

The figure stopped. Under its cloak Twinks could see a bright yellow silken slip.

"I'm Daffodil, can't stop now or I shall be late. My time's up," and the creature was eager to be off.

"But please explain. How do you know it's time?" Twinks was determined to get some kind of answer to her question.

"How do I know?" snapped the daffodil. "Don't you ever wake up at the right time? Why, I know inside me when my time's up without bothering to look at the clock. But I had a sister once who would go up at Snowdrop time and it was so cold she froze and never used any of her proper time again. See you later, perhaps, good-bye," and Daffodil hurried away.

Twinks turned to Mr. Pobblethwaite who by now had wound up the clock and was showing Bill one of the wooden bunks. "What exactly is this place, it's rather like the store-room where my daddy keeps his bulbs and seeds till he wants them in the spring again. Only I thought his bulbs didn't talk or move."

"This is Dame Nature's dormitory, at least one of them," replied Mr. Pobblethwaite. "There are many others where the different creatures rest and sleep till it's time for them to start work again."

"Why is it that some plants stay up out-doors in the garden all through winter?" Bill wanted to know.

"That's only what *you* think," said Mr. Pobblethwaite. "The real part of them is underground, sleeping and getting energy for spring when they have to work so hard."

"Work hard, why, it must be easy doing nothing but grow." Bill smiled at the idea of flowers working.

"Easy," Mr. Pobblethwaite chuckled. "It's very, very hard work growing, I can tell you. There are leaves to unfold, buds to open out and food to get in from the soil. Then the flowers have to help the sun keep their colours bright and take in more nourishment through their leaves; to say nothing of entertaining the bees and other insects that help them make sure of next year's blossoms. It is only when all this work is done that the flowers can take a real rest and gradually steal away to sleep again while their outward forms above ground are fading. And while they rest other workers are turning and tilling the earth to make it ready for spring again."

Bill and Twinks looked thoughtful about this work business. And while they had been listening to Mr. Pobblethwaite, Gaffer Mole and the squirrels had been setting the bunks to rights again.

Suddenly they saw the mole stump across to a dark corner where he bent down and from a pile of leaves dragged out a crumpled-looking bundle.

"Why aren't you a-gone with t'others?" he growled. "Last year 'twas just the same. You'm a lazy young imp, you be. Now be off with yer, I say."

The little bulb whimpered: "But I'm still sleepy, I don't want to grow, I want to stay here and sleep."

"You'd sleep what wits you have away if I let 'ee," answered Gaffer. "Nature ain't put 'ee here to sleep away your time, you've got to go and make more flowers of your own. Cut along now, do," and he shooed the bulb away and up the tall ladder out of sight.

"Fancy there being naughty flowers," said Twinks wonderingly. "That one's time seemed to have gone wrong. How did that happen?"

"The time was all right," replied Mr. Pobblethwaite. "It's not the time's fault if it isn't used in the right way, it's still there just the same."

Before Twinks could say another word a gruff voice boomed down into the room from the hole in the roof where the ladder disappeared.

"Now then, now then, come on, you snowdrops. There are ten of you missing. You, Gaffer, see that they come along quickly.

Bill and Twinks could not see who was talking, but Gaffer Mole had bustled up to some bunks at the far end of the room and was hastily turning out some more little brown bundles.

He seemed very angry and positively chased the poor things down the room and up the ladder.

"Always late, them snowdrops," he muttered when the last one had vanished.

"Always last to go; they'd sleep the year round if I'd let 'em."

"Who was that who called through the roof?" Twinks was one of those girls who must know about everything. Inquisitive, Bill called her. But her father said it was merely that she was of an inquiring turn of mind!

"Who, 'im? That's the gardener, Boffin," answered Gaffer. " 'E 'as to see the garden is ready for spring. That's 'is job, that is. If you go up along you'll maybe have a talk to him. But bless my buttons, look at the time. It'll be cuckoo time before I can turn round." And Gaffer Mole scuttled away, calling to the squirrels to stir their stumps or it would be too late.

Mr. Pobblethwaite pulled a big old-fashioned silver watch out of his pocket. "Yes, it's time for us to be on our way, too. Come, my dears," and he turned to Bill and Twinks, "we have just time enough to have a talk with some of our

[44]

other garden friends down here before Spring comes. We'll take the lift outside, that'll be quicker. . . ."

Still Winter

Have you ever seen an Admiral
Curled up asleep in bed
Without his velvet uniform
All slashed with gold and red?

He looks just like a parcel,
Dusty and brown and torn,
You'd never think that out of *that*
An Admiral could be born!

But it is one of time's old tricks,
Pretending to be dead.
Look out when summer comes again
And the Admiral turns red!

DOWN, down, down into the darkness
went the lift. From a lantern in the roof
a faint light glimmered. But it was a queer

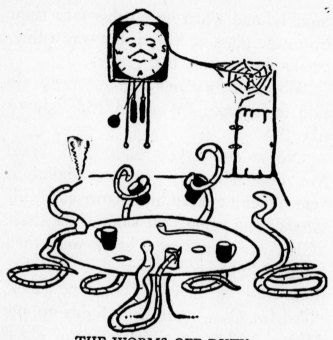

THE WORMS OFF DUTY

Worms, like all else, work hard to do their share of keeping the world in order

light because it kept going on and off, and at one moment the spark was in one corner and the next moment it was in another. When Bill looked at it more closely he discovered that it was moving quite

[47]

quickly, and when he put his face right up to the glass he saw that it was a tiny, beetle-like creature that glowed.

"Why, I believe it's a glow-worm," he said to Twinks. "What an odd light to have!"

"Not so odd as you might think," said Mr. Pobblethwaite, who was finding it very difficult to keep his balance as the lift *would* bang against the sides of the shaft. "Glow-worms are more economical than electric light, you know, because they don't waste heat. By the way," he added, "it's Mrs. Glow-worm who lights up, not Mister. And don't call her a worm—she is a beetle but didn't want legs very much."

Before Bill could reply and while Twinks was investigating the light for herself, the lift came to a dead stop with such a bump that they all fell down like ninepins and the lantern swung so violently that Mrs. Glow-worm was tipped out and scurried away with her light into the darkness.

No sooner had the three picked themselves up and scrambled out of the lift than the door clanged to and the lift shot upwards again.

Mr. Pobblethwaite seemed rather annoyed. He was brushing the dust off his immaculate suit and muttering to himself. "I must tell the Inspector, I must tell the Inspector; can't have the lift behaving like this every time."

Bill and Twinks did not worry their heads about a little dust, they were looking about them to see where they had got to now.

They were in a room, very like the one they had left. Big, and dimly lit by flickering lights which looked remarkably like most glow-worms, because, as Bill said afterwards, "They never kept still for a moment."

The whole room had a funny earthy kind of smell. But the exciting thing was all the curious creatures who were lying or sitting about.

effort to make head or tail of what Mr. Pobblethwaite said was too difficult for her.

Bill then chimed in: "Do let's go and talk to the worms and hear what they have to say. Will they mind if we talk to them?"

"Certainly not, they will welcome you." Mr. Pobblethwaite advanced boldly to the nearest table where some comfortably fat worms were drinking and smoking.

"Excuse me, Ebenezer." He bowed courteously. "My young friends would like to meet you if you could spare them a moment."

The fattest worm who apparently answered to the name of Ebenezer grinned amiably, and Twinks and Bill stepped forward rather nervously. Through their minds ran the sudden thought how perfectly mad it was to be talking to worms. What did one do, what language did one say, how should one behave?

But they need not have worried for

worms know how to put humans at their ease. They drained their tankards and set them on the table with a thud.

"What's in the mugs?" asked Bill.

"Cold milk and water from trees," said their guide, "but don't interrupt him."

Then Ebenezer wriggled out of his chair. Bowing low he pronounced in a gruff tone that he and his friends would be more than delighted to converse with any friends of Mr. Pobblethwaite. As for time —well, their time was at his disposal. With a grandiloquent gesture Ebenezer resumed his seat and all the worms looked inquiringly up at Bill and Twinks.

"Please," Twinks twined her fingers together nervously, a habit she had when anything excited her, "how do you like being down here, and how do you know when it is time to go up above ground again?" She was so eager that the last few words sounded like "abogrogain", all in a rush.

It seemed that to mention time to these under-earth creatures was the cause of great amusement, for the worms wriggled their bodies about in a kind of ecstasy of mirth and queer gurgles of laughter fairly bubbled out of them.

"Ah, time—time—ha, ha, ha, he, he, he," they resolved into perfect paroxysms of delight.

"Dear young lady," replied the fattest and reddest. "Time is something you can use just how and when you want it. Don't ever let time manage you, be sure and control your time. Store it up, make good use of it and you'll be all right."

Another worm took up the thread of conversation. "There's a sort of clock inside us, Missy, that tells us when to go. Reckon you have one inside you too, if you'd only use it." He puffed great clouds of white smoke from his pipe as much as to say, that's that!

But Twinks was not convinced.

"Where is the clock?" she queried. "I

can't see it, unless you mean the one that Mr. Pobblethwaite is winding up" (for that personage had climbed up on a stool and was busy with his winder again).

Another gust of laughter shook the worms.

"No, Missy, you can't see it," they babbled, "but it's there all the same. Sure as time means change we know when it gets to our time. There's something that says to us inside, 'Time to go up along, time to be moving'."

"But," added the smallest worm gravely, pointing with his long pipe at Twinks, "we mustn't be *too* early or we might be caught by the early bird!"

As the worm said that he suddenly stiffened into an attitude of expectancy. Far above their heads Bill and Twinks heard a dull thud, thud, a long way away at first, then getting louder and louder as if all the elephants in the world were playing at leap-frog.

They put their hands to their ears to

block out the fearful noise. The worms paled (at least that's how they looked) as the thuds grew so appalling that the whole room seemed to rock.

The strange thing was that Mr. Pobblethwaite was totally unconcerned. He had wound up the big clock and was stuffing his pipe with some of the tobacco from one of the worms' pouches and apparently did not hear a sound of the noise above. The other creatures as well, spiders, frogs and beetles seemed quite oblivious of the noise.

"What on earth is that row?" screamed Bill into Mr. Pobblethwaite's ear.

The Time Keeper looked astonished. "Row, what row? Oh, I see you must have tuned in to the worms' wavelength, that's the Early Bird, I expect."

"Yes, ye-es, y-s-s," stuttered the worms, "it's the Early Bird, but we're up to his capers, he won't catch us if we can help it," and they wriggled violently about under the table and rolled over the floor in all directions like pocket-sized tanks.

After a bit the noise died down and the worms crowded round the table again and began to search frantically for their pipes which had fallen under the table in all the hurry and scurry.

Now that the fright was over they pretended to be very brave and all chanted together: "He won't catch us, he won't catch us."

Bill whispered to Twinks: "I believe they really are in an awful stew about the Early Bird, but it can't be much fun to be gobbled up for a thrush's breakfast. Still, they're lucky to be able to hear so well that they are warned in time. I hope *he* can't hear quite so well too."

By this time the worms had resumed their seats at the table and were contentedly puffing away at their pipes. Indeed, the room was so thick with mist that it was almost impossible to see across it.

This time it was Bill who put the question.

"When you go up to earth again, what do you do, how do you spend your time?"

This simple remark seemed to flummox the worms completely. They wriggled so convulsively that they looked like agitated concertinas.

"What do we do?" they chorused. "What do we do? Why, we work, we work, we WORK!" and their voices rose to a shrill squeak.

Bill persisted. "What *is* your work?" he asked, unimpressed by the idea of overworked worms.

"Well," said Ebenezer, taking a long, long pull at his pipe. "We're engineers, we irrigate the soil, break up the ground. Last year"—and he patted himself proudly on his swelling chest—"last year hundreds of tons of earth passed through our bodies alone—just think of that, young man. If it wasn't for me and my friends working all day and half the night you'd have no vegetables in your garden, or flowers either for that matter. Work, why we work harder than any other people, I can tell you."

Before the astonished Bill could reply, another worm broke in excitedly:

"Yes, and we've got some French cousins that live and work in trees. They don't do the same work as we do, they're more air-minded than us. And," he added importantly, "I've got some more cousins at the South Pole and they live under the ice. So you see we worm engineers are scattered all over the world. Ours is a *very* fine family."

"Ours is a *very* fine family," shouted all the worms together as if determined there should be no mistake about it.

"Bill and Twinks found their tongues. "Thank you so much for telling us," they said, and feeling that something was wanting to round off these interesting disclosures, and partly to hide their feelings, they shook hands gravely all round with the worms, who seemed only to anxious to show that they were very fine fellows, but not too grand to be friendly with two rather stupid mortals.

At the same moment as they had shaken the hand of the last worm and thought how clammy it felt, up bustled Mr. Pobblethwaite.

"Now, my dears," he exclaimed, "I want you to meet the gossamer spiders, for I think they would interest you both, and I want you to see as many things as possible if time permits." As he said the word "time" Mr. Pobblethwaite looked at Twinks and gave a knowing wink! He was an amazing little man, she thought, for although he was so very important and such a personage with a capital P, he always saw the funny side of everything.

"Who are the gossamer spiders?" Bill asked as they followed Mr. Pobblethwaite across the room, leaving the worms to their own devices.

Mr. Pobblethwaite did not answer but led them to a corner where a collection of spiders were sitting round a circular wooden table working at piles of grey gossamer. Twinks saw that some were winding spools of it and that others were fashioning masses of the soft silken stuff into what looked like huge dust sheets. A few were folding up the work that was finished.

"Good evening to you," said Mr. Pobblethwaite very politely. Twinks nudged Bill and whispered: "He always is so polite, isn't he?" at the same time making a mental note to do the same when dealing with animals and insects, to say nothing of flowers.

"Working hard as usual, I see," went on Mr. Pobblethwaite.

One of the spiders, a fine good-looking insect with big goggling eyes, looked up from her task of carding silk.

"We're well enough, well enough, Mr. Time Keeper. But there's little time to be lost before our time is up," and she bent to her work again.

"What is it that you are making?"

Twinks gently touched the delicate silky stuff that felt like thistledown to her hand.

"That's for when we want to fly away," said the spider, smoothing down the strands of gossamer. "I expect you've seen us ballooning over the fields in the mornings when you've got up specially early. When our call comes we just ups with our parachutes and away we go." She gave a deft flick to a heap of gossamer and it floated up to the roof over their heads like a wisp of smoke.

"How clever you are," Bill and Twinks were admiring. "We'd love to try and fly on one of those."

"That's nothing," nodded the spider. "Why," she went on, "some of my relations are much, much cleverer. Cousin Argyroneta, who lives under water, makes the most bee-u-tiful diving bells you've ever seen."

"Diving bells? Why does she make diving bells?" asked Bill. "What a nice name! Is your cousin Argy a diver?"

"Diver, indeed," the spider positively snorted. "Of course not, she makes the bells to put her babies in when she lays them, 'cos then she knows they are safe. My cousin has lovely clothes too, she always wears silk and velvet, much, much smarter than we are here."

"But she must get awfully wet under water all the time," put in Twinks, who always wanted to find out about everything.

"No, she doesn't," the spider retorted; "her clothes are quite waterproof, and what is more"—here the little creature came very close to Twinks and in a most confidential tone whispered—"she doesn't eat her husbands like lots of us do, so you see how grand she is."

"Eat her husbands, good heavens, you don't mean to say you eat your husbands. How simply dreadful! Why on earth do you do that, can't you get any other food?" Twinks was obviously shaken by the spider's confidences.

"Of course we can get other food." The spider seemed rather taken aback that her story had not gone too well. "But husbands will keep on worrying so and a man about the house is a terrible nuisance, so if they won't get out to work we find it best to eat them up. But they are not very good."

Bill gave Twinks a nudge with his elbow, he felt that if carried on with, this husband business might lead to trouble. So he shyly interposed: "What do you think about time, Mrs. Spider?"

"Time?" The spider scratched her head with two of her legs at once. "Time, that's rather hard to say, but I think it is something you never get enough of, and when it's your time it's not mine and, I'll tell you something, if you try hard enough you can hold time back." She waggled a leg at Bill wisely. "You don't believe me, young man, I can see, but it's true none the less."

"But how do you stop time?" Twinks asked. "If you stopped time, why, the whole world would stop too."

"Indeed it would not," testily answered the spider. "If I am pushed for time I can stop it as easy as making a web."

"Well, tell us how." Twinks refused to be browbeaten by a mere insect and was determined to have the truth.

The spider smoothed down its grey-green dress with a smirking air.

"If I have one minute to finish a job that usually takes three minutes," it said deliberately, "I say to time in my head, now you just stop a minute, hold back, don't go on, and time stops for me if I think hard enough and I can get the work done in the right time. Why, some of my friends are so clever that they can use a revolving circular saw made of web. Perhaps you don't understand, young lady, that if the web could move fast enough it would be hard enough to cut wood. That's just time. You mortals think that you are very clever and talk of us as 'insects', but you could not do without us whatever you may think. Our webs are finer and stronger than anything you can make, and your stargazers are glad to use them for their most wonderful instruments, so there!" The spider began to grow quite red in the face at the thought of all its clever relations.

"Yes," chipped in another one who was folding up the gossamer, "my first cousin twice removed belongs to a family that live on butterflies, and they catch the butterflies by spinning webs that look like bird droppings because they know that the butterflies are partial to them. What do you think of that?" And the little creature positively stamped on the floor with all its legs at once and the other spiders chimed in with cries of "Hear, hear".

Twinks opened her mouth to speak, but the spider evidently thought enough time had been wasted in talking, for it suddenly grabbed up a heap of gossamer and before Twinks could say another word had disappeared.

"Oh dear," Twinks sighed. "This time

business. Mr. Pobblethwaite—if everyone and everything in the world has a time of its own, why is it that everything isn't hopelessly muddled up? If I wanted to keep an appointment with a worm and he went by his time and I went by mine we would both turn up at different times."

Mr. Pobblethwaite roared with laughter till his fat sides shook.

"You'd meet all right," he told her, because two times would see to that; never mind now, let us go and find Bill."

While Twinks had been talking to the spider, Bill had wandered away into the gloom of the big hall. As he stopped a moment under a grating high up on the wall he heard a strange medley of sounds coming from somewhere on the other side. There were shrill squeaks, chirpings and twitterings which gradually resolved themselves into words and sentences. Bill caught the words: "Hen's place is in the nest, not on the treetops—disgraceful— horriferous." Then came much fluttering of wings and more squeaks as if a fight was going on.

Bill was intrigued. The grating was too high for him to reach, but at the side was a small door that looked promising. Bill pushed it gently and to his surprise it was not locked. He looked round to see Twinks and Mr. Pobblethwaite still talking, so he deftly edged his way through the doorway.

There were birds everywhere. They were perched on chairs and tables and cupboards and were all turned towards a large brown owl who sat on the top of a small platform and was haranguing the rest.

"Keep to the nest indeed," twittered a thrush. "What do they think we are! What I say is we must have equal rights with our husbands."

At that a terrific chattering went up from one half of the assembly, while the others groaned.

The owl, peering through enormous spectacles, hooted:

[68]

"I propose that we pass a resolution to the effect that every mother bird shall have at least two hours off duty each day and that papa birds shall during that time attend to the young. Speaking for myself, I need a rest. I have to make parcels out of most things I eat."

"I second most of that," shrieked a jay. "Hurrah, hurrah!" shrilled the others, and a tumult of twitters and peeps arose.

Suddenly in the middle of the hubbub a thrush sang out: "I hear worms," and in a moment the noise died down. Bill thought of the crowd of worms in the next room and wondered if the birds would try to make a sudden onslaught and whether he ought to run back and warn the worms that birds were about.

But before he could make up his mind what to do there was the sound of a clock striking and a voice called out: "Time for birds, time for birds." All the birds hustled together excitedly tweeting and fluttering. "It's spring-time, it's spring-time, we know the way, we've got our maps, we must be off, we must be off." Opposite where Bill stood was a window high up in the wall. It was open wide, showing a glimpse of blue skies and white rolling clouds. With one accord the birds spread their wings and like a rushing wind they flew out of the window and were gone.

"Well, of all the odd things," muttered Bill. "P'raps I'd better go back and find Twinks and Mr. P., they may have gone too." He opened the little door again and found himself back in the big hall.

He looked about. Twinks, Mr. Pobblethwaite and Gaffer Mole were having a heated argument with the frogs at the billiard table, although it was still quite cold. Bill went up and pulled at Twinks' arm. "I say," he told her confidentially, "I've been listening to the birds next door. They've flown away now, it's nearly spring-time. Why don't these creatures in here go off too?"

The frogs heard the word "spring-time". "What's that?" they croaked, "spring-time, our clocks have not struck yet but we'd better be getting ready," and they began to put their cues in the racks and the balls in the pockets of the table.

While they were doing this a bell clanged and Gaffer Mole began chanting: "Frogs' time, frogs' time. Please leave all billiard balls for beetles, please leave all . . ."

But with hops, leaps and bounds the frogs shot out of the room and they could be heard chattering as they crowded into the lift, the murmurings growing fainter and fainter as they went upwards.

"Bill"—Twinks put her hand to her head wonderingly—"do you feel anything here?" and she tapped her forehead.

"Feel anything?" Bill was mystified. "No, but wait a minute." He stopped. "Why, Twinks, it's just as if there *was* a voice saying it's time, it's time, it's time, and yet there can't really be a voice. Can you hear it too?"

"Of course I can." Twinks turned to Mr. Pobblethwaite. "Is this what the flowers and insects and animals feel when it's time for them to go up to earth again? Do you feel it?" and she grew more and more excited.

Mr. Pobblethwaite drew out his massive watch again before he answered. "Yes, that's right," he said, "you must have felt it before. When you want to do anything at any special time you feel in your mind when it is that time. It's the same with everything. When it's time for the under-world to wake up they know it perfectly well. They really have no need for those clocks to strike. When it's time the clocks strike in their heads, not out loud. But I let you and Bill hear the clocks so that you could understand better."

At that moment Gaffer Mole, who had been talking to the beetle who sat under the clock to see that everyone got away in good order, came stumping over to them.

"Guess you'd better be moving along," he grumbled. "Not much longer before spring comes, and if your young folk'd like to see the weather room, there'd just about be time, if you'm quick."

Twinks clapped her hands. "Oh, lovely," she cried, "fancy seeing storms made, how thrilling," and she began to tug Bill along towards the door.

Mr. Pobblethwaite hurriedly replaced his watch and began to walk towards the entrance. Bill and Twinks noticed that the room was by now so.thick with smoke that they could not see across it. Mr. Pobble-thwaite took their hands and began to hurry, the walls and even the floor over which they ran began to fade and disappear.

When they reached the door the last thing they heard was the hoarse voice of the Gaffer and the din of the beetle banging on his big drum. . . .

Only
Just Still Winter

"Preposterous!" cried Mr. P. "I know it will
  not rain,
The sun is bright, the moon is out, the clouds
  have gone to Spain."
Then dust flew up, the rain came down, and so
  the poor old fella
Got very wet because he'd not put up his big
  umbrella!

How they got there Bill and Twinks *never*
discovered. All they knew was that one
moment they were in the big hall and the
.next .they were standing in quite a different place! And when they said to Mr. Pobblethwaite: "How on earth did it hap-

FROGS' PLAYTIME

All creatures work and all need rest. Insects and flowers live
happily by being busy in their very own special way

pen?" that happy man simply smiled and
said rather pompously: "A trick of time,
just a trick of time."

[75]

Everything looked very beautiful, and very cold, for, from the roof and walls of the vast chamber where they stood, hung glittering icicles. Not clear, white ones, but of all colours of the rainbow. The floor was carpeted with snow and Bill noticed with delight that when he spoke his breath frosted and then floated up into the air like wisps of smoke.

He looked at Twinks and then guffawed.

"What's the matter, silly, what's funny about me?" Twinks asked.

"Look at your clothes." Bill pointed at her and then roared with laughter again, until he happened to look down at his own body and then he just gasped with astonishment.

Both of them were wearing blue boiler suits, all made in one piece like a workman's, but they looked as if they were slightly inflated all over, and felt deliciously warm.

"They're like hot-water bottles," giggled Twinks. Mr. Pobblethwaite looked like nothing so much as a round india-rubber ball that might bounce up to the ceiling at any moment.

"You can make them hotter or colder as you wish," he said, pointing to a tiny valve at one side of the suits.

At once Twinks and Bill started to twist the valve tops and sure enough they felt their bodies getting hotter and fatter at the same time!

"What fun! Let's see who can get the fattest." Bill twisted his valve violently and felt his feet begin to float off the floor.

"Look out, young man," warned Mr. Pobblethwaite, if you blow up too much you'll only burst and then freeze until you're an icicle."

So they turned the taps the other way till at length they were moderately warm and moderately fat.

The hall they were in was enormous, so big that they could not see the other end of it. Everywhere they looked was machinery. Huge shining engines whizzing round at terrific speed, giant pistons chugging up and down, and bright cylinders whirring along well-oiled rods.

There were numbers of keen-faced men darting about from engine to engine, some with polishing rags in their hands, others with cans of queer mixture, and all of them far too engrossed to pay any attention to the three visitors.

Above a clock on the wall near them was a notice that read: "Weather Generating Station." "Do they make weather here?" Bill asked. "I'd love to see storms made." "And rain, wind and mist," put in Twinks. "Can we have a look round, Mr. P.?"

"Wait here a moment, I'll get hold of the foreman, Jack Frost," said Mr. Pobblethwaite, and he trotted in and out of the giant machines looking more like a rubber ball than ever.

Twinks turned to Bill. "You know, Bill, it's very mysterious how we've got here," she remarked thoughtfully. "A second ago we were up on the ground walking on the downs, now we're down here with Mr. P. talking to spiders and worms. Goodness knows what Mother will say when we get home, that's to say if we ever do get home again."

"Don't be a silly ass," Bill was convincing, "of course we'll get home; I think this is a marvellous adventure. I'm sure I shall be quite fond of worms and things when I am on earth again. Probably this is all a dream and we shall wake up in a minute. But," he added, "I don't want to wake up for ages and ages. I want to see all round the year before I go back again."

He broke off abruptly for Mr. Pobblethwaite had rolled up again and with him was one of the men they had seen tending the engines.

"This is Foreman Jack Frost," introduced Mr. Pobblethwaite, and Bill and Twinks shook hands politely as if it was a matter of everyday occurrence to be introduced to someone who in their wildest dreams they had never thought to meet.

Jack Frost was slender and tanned as if he spent his life outdoors instead of inside looking after engines. To distinguish him from the other workers he wore a square white cap.

"Pleased to meet you," he said in crisp tones, and as he shook hands brilliant blue sparks shot out. He smiled at Twinks' astonishment as she drew back from him.

"Full of electricity I am, Missy," he said, and took her hand again and at once a vivid spark flashed between them.

"Rather frightening, I think," Twinks said, "if every time you shake hands or touch anything you burst into flame."

Jack Frost laughed, and when he did so his laugh crackled in points of blue flame.

"Don't you worry, Missy, I'm a careful

sort of bloke, I am, and never goes a-pokin'
my head in where it is not wanted."

"Now, Mr. Frost," Mr. Pobblethwaite
spoke in his politest tones, "while I'm attending to the clock yonder perhaps you'll
be kind enough to let my two young friends
see you weather-makers at work. But I'm
afraid we cannot stay very long because
time is flying and we have a long round to
make. Look!" and he pointed to the door
at one end of the chamber.

Twinks and Bill turned quickly and
caught a fleeting glimpse of something
that looked like a bird flying through the
open doorway.

"Why, what's that?" they chorused.

"Time flying!" answered Mr. Pobblethwaite, and seeing their utter amazement
he roared with laughter so that Jack Frost
joined in and the two of them exchanged
glances as much as to say they had some
secret joke between themselves.

Twinks was rather annoyed. "If you

know Time is flying, why don't you stop him? You remember what the spider told us. You *can* stop time if you try to."

"But you've got to catch him on the hop," remarked Mr. Pobblethwaite. "You can't wait to look after him. You must catch him as he comes up. Perhaps we'll get another chance later on. But Time is a crafty fellow. Let him know you want to catch him and he'll fly past like lightning, or even quicker to-morrow, but if he thinks you don't want him he'll dawdle about till you're sick of the sight of him. Anyhow, you two had better look around while I see that the clock is in order," and Mr. Pobblethwaite trundled off holding his big winding handle that he had produced like a rabbit from a hat, only this came from the pocket of his boiler suit.

"Now, Missy," it was Jack Frost who spoke, "seeing as how his Nibs has left you to my care, perhaps you would like to see how we work things for Nature down here. She's been at it so long that she is always right. So come this way and I'll let you raise a storm—that's if you're a good girl," and he gave Twinks a cheery grin.

"Make a storm? I should jolly well think I would like to," replied Twinks. "Goodness, what a fearsome-looking thing!"

They had come up in front of the biggest machine in the place. It towered to the ceiling, a mass of intricate cables, cylinders and swift-turning wheels. In front, on a level with their heads, was an enormous instrument-board, something like that on a motor-car but hundreds of times larger. On this were brass knobs and handles all labelled underneath with such words as: Thunder, Rain, Snow, Winds. Above was a highly-polished mirror which, strangely enough, reflected nothing at all although they all stood facing it.

"Now," said Jack Frost, "what would you like to see first?"

"Lightning, snow," cried Twinks and Bill together.

Jack Frost leaned forwards and pulled the lever over the storm section. At once a deep, reverberating roar filled the hall. It echoed from floor to ceiling, getting louder and louder. At the same moment the surface of the mirror dimmed, then cleared, and to their astonishment they saw a reflection of the downs and Mr. Pobblethwaite's shop. But the sky was dark and threatening, and as they looked, lightning cut across it and a lashing squall of rain followed.

Then with another quick pull Jack Frost set the lever again into motion; the roar of thunder died away, the rain ceased and the surface of the mirror cleared.

"How do you do it?" eagerly asked Twinks. "Can't I have a try at something. Please, dear Jack Frost, let me make a snowstorm?"

"Right you are, Missy. Here, pull this

handle," and Jack Frost showed her where to hold the lever above the word "Snow".

Twinks gave a valiant tug with both hands and the lever began slowly to move down. The mirror clouded over again and over the downs and Mr. Pobblethwaite's shop swept a snowstorm covering the whole landscape with a white cloud.

Of course, after this, Bill wanted to try, and snowstorms, rain, hail and winds rushed across the mirror in quick succession.

"It's all too, too marvellous," Twinks said at last. "I can't understand anything of how it all happens, but I suppose the weather is all there somehow and you just make it start when it's wanted?"

"Something like that, Miss," smiled Jack Frost. "Now watch me play a joke on the Time Keeper," and he turned to speak to Mr. Pobblethwaite who had finished with the clock and now came up polishing the iron clock handle with his silk handkerchief.

[85]

"You wouldn't think it was goin' to rain, sir, now would you?" asked Jack Frost.

Mr. Pobblethwaite gave a quick look at the big mirror and saw that it was clear.

"No, Jack," he said. "Weather looks set fair for the moment. Good thing as I left my umbrella in Gaffer Mole's place."

"Well, sir, you'll be surprised to know that there's a shower on the way and you'd better take shelter, for here it comes."

With these words Jack Frost threw up into the air a handful of dust that he took from a bucket standing by the wall. Up went the dust and down came quite a sharp shower of rain. So heavy, in fact, that Mr. Pobblethwaite ran for shelter under one of the big machines while Bill and Twinks stood and laughed at him

"That's a good trick, how do you do it?" Bill asked as Mr. Pobblethwaite scrambled back again from under the engine, and shook his fist at Jack Frost, laughing all the time.

"It's no trick," declared Jack Frost, "it's only what goes on up above but on a smaller scale."

"But no one throws dust up in the air every time before it rains," grumbled Twinks. "I don't understand at all."

"No, they don't, but the dust is there already," Jack told her. "You see, the air gets damp and the dampness 'sticks' on to the bits of dust that float about and then they get so wet and heavy that at last they fall as rain."

"But I still don't see how the dust gets there," persisted Twinks. "I've never noticed that the air is full of dust when it's a wet day. I'm sure it always feels wet, not dry."

Jack Frost turned to Mr. Pobblethwaite who was gingerly fingering the polished surface of one of the giant cylinders. "The air is full of dust, isn't it, Time Keeper? Shouldn't get much rain otherwise, should we?"

"Oh, certainly, certainly," Mr. Pobble-thwaite assured him, "of course there's dust in the air. I'm always arranging for somewhere to be hot so that there'll be a wind somewhere else. Why, there's dust from the ground; every time you walk you kick up a dust. Then the winds raise a dust; when you ride your pony you make a dust; storms whip up dust from the sea shore and the deserts. Volcanoes simply ooze dust, and every shooting star that streaks across the sky brings a small cloud of dust with it. No dust, pooh, psah! Don't be ridiculous, child, the whole air reeks of dust."

Twinks was taken aback by Mr. Pobble-thwaite's vehemence.

"I never knew *that*," she said, "but I'm sure if I threw up a handful of dust it wouldn't rain—now would it?"

"Well, Missy," smiled Jack Frost, "it *might* not. There's a spot of electricity wanted too; sure, it wouldn't quite do if anyone who wanted to could start a wet day. Nature would have something to say to that, I'm thinking."

Bill broke in: "What makes rainbows, Jack? You seem to know everything about these things, so please explain."

Jack looked thoughtful. "Well," he said, "daylight is really rainbow colours mixed and light has a lot to do with time."

Bill laughed. "Oh dear," he complained, "there it goes again."

"No," replied Jack, "it's not so difficult. If you look at some flowers the colour is because all the other colours are soaked up except the one your eyes can see, but a fly's gauzy wing shows colour because the wing is so thin that it chops up the daylight into a rainbow."

Bill seemed very surprised. "I'd like to know about colours, wouldn't you, Twinks? but I still want to make a rainbow."

Jack Frost chuckled and snapped his fingers till blue fire ran between them.

He darted to the big instrument board

[89]

and pulled out a shiny knob. "Look!" He pointed to the mirror and across its surface arched a rainbow.

"Now watch, I'll show you how a rainbow happens."

As he spoke, the rainbow faded and in its place appeared a heavy shower of rain falling. Then, while they looked, rays of sunshine shot across the mirror, and as the rays fell on to the raindrops they were bent aside and split up into different colours, and these colours blended together to form the exquisite curve of the rainbow.

"How beautiful!" Twinks' eyes were wide with excitement. "I do understand now. When Mummy's ring sparkles with colours like a rainbow it's because the light gets all broken up. But then," she looked puzzled, "why isn't the whole world just full of rainbows, light must keep on hitting things all the time?"

"That's true, Missy," agreed Jack Frost, "but you see, the water of the raindrops is like a mirror, it reflects the sunshine in a way that other more solid things, like tables and chairs wouldn't do. Every drop of rain is a tiny lens all on its own. There's a lot to learn about old Mrs. Nature. Perhaps one day the Time Keeper will take you for a trip under the earth. It's wonderful down there. Pretty hot though," he added, "you'd have to be careful because it's only the top of the earth pie that's cool, the inside is a molten mass floating on even hotter stuff. If you went there you'd have to wear asbestos suits or you'd burn up in a flash."

Bill nudged Twinks and whispered: "Ask him about time, he's sure to know."

But before Twinks had time to say another word Mr. Pobblethwaite had taken his watch out, and, saying that they had exactly half a second more in which to talk to Jack Frost, began to stroll in a leisurely manner towards a door at the other side of the room.

"Please, before we have to go, can you tell us anything about time?" asked Twinks hurriedly. "You see, we're awfully anxious to find out what time really is. We've asked the worms and the spiders, and Mr. Pobblethwaite, but they all seem to have their own time, and they're not very good at explaining to us, can you help us, Mr. Jack Frost?"

Jack Frost began to laugh, and as he laughed his cheeks crackled, and from every part of his body flickered blue and green sparks till he seemed as if he must burst out into a bonfire.

"I can't see what's so funny about time," said Twinks to Bill. "We must be awfully silly, because all these underearth people laugh at us."

Jack Frost was calming down, and at length he had recovered enough to speak.

"Sorry, Missy," he gulped, "but it's all the same, whenever the Time Keeper brings along his friends they always want to know about time. There isn't any time, you see, that's why it's so difficult to explain about it."

"Isn't any time?" Twinks was more mystified than ever. "But Mr. P. just said we had only half a second to talk to you in, and that must have gone ages ago."

"Yes, it must have gone a thousand years ago, or it may not have gone at all," replied Jack Frost. "Probably the Time Keeper has still got it for you, otherwise you wouldn't still be talking to me, would you?"

"How can he have got our time, if there isn't any time to get?"

Twinks began to get annoyed, she hated not to understand a thing and this time business was beyond a joke.

"Well, you haven't got any time of your own now, have you?" Jack Frost asked her. "My time is up there," and he pointed to the clock on the wall. "The Time Keeper always sets my time very slow as I have so much work to do, otherwise I wouldn't get through it all in time."

"But don't you ever take time off, don't you ever sleep?" asked Bill. "You must get awfully tired sometimes looking after all this weather."

"Yes, I do sleep sometimes, but not for more than a second at a time," said Jack Frost.

"A second at a time, but that can't possibly be any good. Why, as soon as you shut your eyes it would be time to open them again."

"That's just what does happen," said Jack Frost emphatically. "There's no time in sleep, you can sleep a year in a flash, that's just the beauty of it. I shut my eyes and in a second I've slept for half a year and then I'm ready for tons and tons more work again."

Seeing that his visitors still looked puzzled, Jack Frost pointed to the clock again. The big pendulum was hanging at an angle of 45 degrees and seemed to have stuck, for it did not fall back again to its usual place.

"The Time Keeper sets my clock so slow," said Jack Frost, "that the pendulum takes a month to swing. Once, when Nature wanted all sorts of bad weather at the same time, he had to come along and set it to fast. We *did* have a time then, I can tell you, all the men—and me—were dancing about so fast that we got hot and almost melted."

"My goodness," said Twinks, "what a business."

"Yes, it was indeed," Jack Frost meditated. . . . "But I don't mind, I like snow because it ploughs the ground and gives worms a chance to see it's well drained, and rain is grand. . . . Food for flowers, *I* call it."

"Food?" asked Bill.

"Yes, the rain takes food out of the earth to young seeds and helps the food they carry in their own haversack."

At that moment Mr. Pobblethwaite

reached the door, and as he turned and called out, "Time to come; hurry up, you two," Bill and Twinks felt some invisible hand give them a quick push towards him, and before they could say good-bye to Jack Frost and his men, they were whirled away. . . .

Spring

"Papa, I'm sure it's time to start,"
The youngest cuckoo said.

But Poppa Cuckoo spoke no word,
He only shook his head.

"Papa, I know it's time to go,"
The eldest cuckoo cried,

"I want to fly to Africa
And choose my next year's bride."

Then Poppa Cuckoo answered them:
"Be off you two to bed,

I'll tell you that it's time to leave
When the clock strikes in my head."

"How on earth did we get here? I do declare it's a wood!"
Twinks looked about her curiously. The

[97]

THE WEATHER FACTORY

*Weather keeps all living things fresh and well. It rests tired
flowers and helps the earth to prepare for Spring*

Weather Generating Station had disappeared, so had Jack Frost, and in place of
the engines and mirror there were trees,
trees, trees, all round them.

Bill was looking for birds' nests as if it was a matter of every-day occurrence to be swept from place to place, and Mr. Pobblethwaite sat on a fallen tree trunk polishing his watch with his pocket handkerchief. Twinks noticed, too, that he had his umbrella with him. "I expect he just magicked it up from Gaffer Mole," she thought. "I'll never be surprised at anything that happens to me now. I'll bet he found it by wireless."

"Where are we?" she asked Mr. Pobblethwaite, seating herself down beside him. "What are we going to see here? I do think you might have told us we were going to be swept along like this. We never even had time to say good-bye to Jack Frost."

"I warned you, you only had half a second to spare," answered the Time Keeper rather severely. "Don't be impatient, child. This is Cuckoo Wood and I've brought you here because it's nearly springtime, and if you keep on your spectacles you'll be able to see the underworld people coming up."

Twinks put her hand up to her eyes. The spectacles were there all right, although she couldn't feel them resting on her nose. But when she looked at Bill there was no sign of his.

"Bill, where are your specs?" she cried. "You'll miss seeing all the excitement if you haven't got them on."

Bill turned. "Don't fuss, mine are all right, and he put his hand to his face. Twinks got up from the tree and went up to him and when she put her hand up to his eyes, sure enough she could feel them too.

"That's a lovely twisty ivy," she went on, running her hand up the trunk of a giant oak that looked as if it must be thousands of years old.

"Lovely ivy?" snorted Mr. Pobble-thwaite. "Take another look at it, it's the tree's deadliest enemy. You'd soon see what was happening if time speeded it up. Why, there's a battle on between the tree and the ivy all the time."

He took out his watch again and turned the hands.

"Now look at the ivy," he commanded.

The two looked intently. At first nothing seemed to be happening. Then, as they watched, the mighty tree gave a convulsive shudder like a wrestler does when he strains to loosen the hold of his opponent. The huge trunk swelled and strained as the twisting tendrils of the ivy gripped and clutched, its curling cruel fingers pressing into the bark.

It was terrible. Twinks shuddered, it was like watching a snake coil itself round the body of its victim. Hard as the mighty tree braced and put out all its strength it was useless against the rapidly climbing ivy.

Then suddenly Bill pulled himself together, whipped out a knife from his pocket and began hacking at the twining roots. Twinks tried to help him and between them they managed to tear away with their fingers some of the finer ivy threads. Bill edged his knife blade underneath and with a strong slicing cut severed the thick fibrous stem. As he did so a shrill scream rent the air, the ivy began to shrivel up before their astonished eyes, and a deep, kindly voice said: "Thank you, young man, that's a good deed you've done. Ivy is sometimes a bad enemy, and unless you'd come along he'd have beaten me in the end."

Twinks and Bill looked up to see where the voice came from. Then they found that it was the oak tree that was talking to them and that, somehow, the huge trunk, the branches and the twigs all made up the figure of a giant that towered over them. He seemed quite gentle and friendly.

"That's all right," Bill answered. "Now I know what ivy can do I'll take jolly good

care that I cut down every piece I see behaving badly."

"Good boy," said the oak. "I'm pretty
strong," and it stretched out its big arms
and they saw the knotted muscles standing
out in thick strands, "but once ivy gets her
clutches on one of us we can do little to
help ourselves."

"Now that you've met my friends, would
you let them see your works?" Mr. Pobblethwaite, who had all this time been
watching Bill and Twinks, now got up
from his seat and walked up to the oak tree.

The tree bent its rugged, good-humoured
face towards the two. "Why, I'd be proud
to show them anything I can," it answered
readily. "Do you think you'd like to see
my factory?"

"Your factory? Why, is there a factory
inside you?" Bill asked. "What on earth
do you do with it?"

"Ha, ha!" boomed the oak. "That's a
good joke, what do I do with it indeed;

[103]

you come along inside and you shall see for yourselves," and it pointed with one of its knobbly fingers to a small circular hole in its trunk. "Just walk in and you can see it all."

Mr. Pobblethwaite led the way, Twinks and Bill followed after, holding each other rather tightly in case they got lost.

There were two steps just inside the hole and when they had gone down these they were able to see better the kind of place a tree factory was. Funny, they thought, to be inside a tree; funny, but jolly interesting too.

"Massa and little Missy let Nobby show them round, please," a gentle voice sounded in their ears, and a big lantern revealed a small creature standing in front of them holding it.

"I believe you're an acorn," cried Twinks.

"Yes, Missy, I'm Nobby Acorn," the little man replied. "Massa Oak tell me to show you everythin' you want to see down here."

Stretching all round them in every direction were enormous pipes, rather like those Twinks and Bill saw sometimes when the roads were under repair.

"What on earth are those?" they asked.

"Massa Oak, he get his food through those, they go long way down, down into the ground and bring up water right up into branches and leaves to the very tip top." Nobby waved his arms so expressively that the lantern nearly went out and Mr. Pobblethwaite had to fix the glow-worm again as it had disappeared into one corner.

"The oak must be awfully strong and he must work awfully hard to draw up water like that," Twinks asked Mr. Pobble-thwaite.

"Everything in nature works hard," he answered. "You seem to think that only human beings work, or think. Insects and

trees and flowers are just as fond of thinking as you are. Trees keep the air fresh,
they also have to think how they can fight
the ivy, how they can draw their food from
the ground and how to protect themselves
from fungi and wicked insects."

"How do they protect themselves?" Bill
was curious, and just at that moment they
heard a loud rat-a-tat-tat at the door
through which they had come.

In a moment Nobby had set the lantern
on the floor and darted to the entrance.
They heard excited twitterings and whis-
perings, then Nobby's voice saying:
"Thank you, thank you, Mister Woodpecker. I'll tell the Master just as quick as
I possibly can."

"What was that, Nobby?" inquired Mr.
Pobblethwaite when Nobby appeared
again.

"Sure 'twas the woodpecker, Mr. Time
Keeper," answered Nobby. "He come to
tell Master that them beetles has been at

work again and shall him kill them all off? I says to him, I says, 'Kill 'em all you can and the Master will be right obliged'."

Mr. Pobblethwaite explained. "There are some beetles," he said, "that bore into the outside of trees and do a great deal of harm. But luckily the woodpeckers are very clever birds and like to eat these beetles, so when they see them they always knock up trees and get permission to eat up the beetles and so help the trees."

"Would Missy and Master like to go downstairs and watch how the tree draws up its water?" queried Nobby.

"Yes, yes," chorused Bill and Twinks.

"Well, while you're downstairs," said Mr. Pobblethwaite, "I'll have a look at the clock, and then when I'm ready I'll give you a call."

Nobby led the way to a flight of steep, dark stairs that seemed to lead down into the bowels of the earth. Twinks had often heard that expression but never quite understood what it meant. But whatever it was, these stairs seemed to lead down to it, or so she thought.

Down and down they went, following the gleam of Nobby's lantern. Then, when Twinks had just made up her mind to go no further, they came to a full stop and saw in front of them a brightly-lit room.

"This is where the Master gets his water through," Nobby told them.

The giant pipes were stretching through this room also but here they were transparent and they could see right through them. As they looked they saw pail after pail ·of water fastened to pulleys being mysteriously drawn upwards. Sometimes the pulleys stopped moving for a moment, then, after a pause, the whole tree seemed to take a deep breath and up would go the pails again.

"It's very wonderful," said Twinks. "How old is Mr. Oak, Nobby?"

"Close on four hundred years he be," Nobby said proudly.

"Four hundred years!" Bill opened his eyes wider and wider. "Fancy being as old as that. Why, he must be tired out with living so long."

"He's not tired out, Master, he lives slower'n you do, much slower. Why, he's a child for ninety years, just you remember that." Nobby was rather scornful.

"But," persisted Bill, "doesn't he ever sleep? Think of all the time he has to pass."

Nobby scratched his brown head thoughtfully. "Time passes all the same, after all, it's only change. Spring, summer, autumn, winter—them makes time. When you and Missy change, then you'll know that time has passed—then you'll know."

"Come along up," called Mr. Pobblethwaite from above, "or you'll miss the cuckoo. Hurry up now."

Led by Nobby, Bill and Twinks hustled up the steep stairs again and scrambled out of the doorway to find Mr. Pobblethwaite deep in conversation with the oak.

Twinks looked up at the tree. "I think you're awfully clever, the way you get your food up from the ground. Whatever made you think of it?"

The old oak smiled. "I have to use my wits," it said. "I learnt it from some sea-weed. And when my time is up I shall go right back into the earth again to make oil and coal. Nearly all the coal and oil you use at home come from my ancestors, and I shall go down into the ground again to do the same work. Nothing is wasted, Lassy, not even time." Here the tree gave a deep, hearty laugh.

Twinks laughed too. As she did so she noticed that a change had come over the tree. Its rough coat, almost the colour of Daddy's old shooting coat, she thought, had turned a different colour. The branches, too, had changed. They were covered with pinkish tufts and brightish green knobs. She looked at the other trees. They, too, were changing colour.

"It's like that transformation scene at

the pantomime," Bill cried. "What's going to happen now, Mr. Pobblethwaite?"

"If you're not too impatient you will see for yourself. Come and sit down and possess your soul in patience."

Bill and Twinks sat down on the tree trunk, one on each side of the Time Keeper, and waited.

"Look!" Twinks jogged Bill's elbow. "Things seem to be waking up."

A toad sat blinking at them from the flat top of a stone, lit up by gleams of pale sunlight that filtered through the branches of the trees. On an alder nearby a thrush began to sing, the clear notes rising like a bugle call. Some bees buzzed across the clearing and under a cluster of green leaves Twinks saw a violet smooth out the crumpled folds of its purple frock.

"Yes, everything seems coming alive again, and our clothes have changed too." Bill pointed to his own soft, green suit, and Twinks saw that in place of their heavy coats they now wore garments gentle to the touch and light to wear.

Mr. Pobblethwaite still wore his white suit but in his buttonhole was a daffodil which gave him an unusually gay look.

He took out his watch and consulted it. "Ah!" he ejaculated, "it's just time; I thought so, here she comes!" and he looked up expectantly.

Into the little clearing where they sat came a little old lady. She wore an old-fashioned poke bonnet tied under her chin with bright ribbons. Over her dark green dress was a white apron, her black shoes were fastened with silver buckles; in her hands she carried a large rush basket with a lid.

No sooner had she come into sight than the little wood burst into life and movement. Birds flew down from the trees; bees and insects hummed in the air and from every nook and cranny peeped flowers and green shoots. They could not describe it, but as Twinks said to Bill afterwards, "the whole place woke up!"

The little old lady did not stop although birds and insects flew about her. She tripped lightly up to Mr. Pobblethwaite.

"Not late, Mr. Time Keeper, am I?" she asked gaily. "Just in time, just in time. I've got him safely, and now we need not wait another minute. Ready, steady, go." She threw open the lid of the basket and with a whir and a flapping of wings a large blue-grey bird flew out and up into the air.

"Cuckoo, cuckoo, cuckoo," echoed around. "Cuckoo, cuckoo!"

The little lady gave a curtsey to Mr. Pobblethwaite. "That's a good job done," she said with satisfaction, "now spring can come along as soon as she likes. And I must be off again, I've got to see that everything's ready for the swallows, too, when they get back. So good-day to you, Mr. Time Keeper," and with another bob the old lady vanished into the trees.

"What does it all mean?" asked Twinks, while Bill was trying to listen to two frogs who were agreeing to go down to the river together.

"It's just an old custom, my dear," Mr. Pobblethwaite told her. "When Mistress Quince lets the cuckoo out of the basket it means that spring is here, so we may expect her at any time now."

At that moment the cuckoo flapped down from the oak tree's topmost branch where he had been surveying the countryside and perched close to Mr. Pobblethwaite on a small silver birch sapling. Twinks saw that he was a fine, handsome bird, evidently quite certain that he was superior to any of the other smaller birds that were twittering round about him.

"Good morning, Mr. Cuckoo." Twinks put on her most Sunday morning manner. "How did you find your way across the sea? You don't mind my asking, do you," she added, "but Bill and I—Bill's my brother, you know—have always been thrilled when we first heard you, but no one could ever tell us how you knew when to come, or how you managed to come so far."

The cuckoo stuck up his big tail boastfully.

"You wouldn't understand, child," he clucked. "Hundreds and hundreds of years ago my ancestors flew from the shores of the Mediterranean sea to lay their eggs in your country. They knew when to start and when to fly back again. When you're hungry you know it's time to eat, don't you? When I'm hungry I know when to start off again. I just start flying and go on flying, with an occasional rest till I get to where I want to. If you *must* know, I add up things in my brain."

And the cuckoo preened itself haughtily.

Twinks was disconcerted. There was that wretched time business creeping in again. She hesitated a minute, then blurted out:

[115]

"Why does Mrs. Cuckoo always lay her eggs in someone else's nest, don't either of you know how to make one of your own?"

At this last question the cuckoo went absolutely spiky with rage. Twinks looked quite frightened. But it appeared to swallow its anger after a second or two and then it replied:

"If other birds are willing to bring up my children that's their affair. It's my work to tell the world that spring is come and I have no time to mess about with fledgelings. My ancestors never did and I don't either," and with this parting shot the cuckoo flew off indignantly to the top of the oak.

"Take two coos, Taffy, take two coos, Taffy," sang a gentle voice in her ear.

Twinks turned quickly and close by on the overhanging branch of a birch sat a beautiful bird with grey plumage.

Twinks smiled. "I'm afraid I annoyed the cuckoo," she said, "but all the same

I did want to know how he migrates far and why he never has a home of his own."

"Coo-oo, coo-oo," went the pigeon. "What long words you use. Can't you use simple words. It's something inside him that tells him when to come and go. If you had your eyes covered you would still be able to find your way a bit. We're cleverer than you, though, we integrate it in our brains. Every turning is rays of time and we use those."

Twinks shook her head. "That's easy for you, Pigeon, but awfully hard for us to understand, because if we want to go across the sea we have to build a boat or an aeroplane to take us, and without a compass we couldn't find our way even then."

"Well, I said we were much cleverer than you, didn't I?" cooed the pigeon, preening its smooth, shining wings. "Far better to have it all in your head, like we have. Pooh, how stupid mortals are, to be sure," and it flew serenely off to a neighbouring tree, calling: "Take two coos, Taffy," as it went.

Mr. Pobblethwaite, who had been listening, now joined in.

"Don't be disheartened, my dear," he told Twinks. "Birds are always a bit airy and disinclined to talk. The truth is they don't really know themselves how it's all done, any more than a baby knows why it walks. But they do say that when nesting time comes near they feel an urge to move, just like when the summer holidays come you and Bill long to go to the seaside."

"That's easier to understand, that is," Twinks said. "I s'pose that when the days get shorter they know then that they simply must get to the sun again as quickly as possible. Like my Aunt Lucie who always says she must follow the sun, and goes in the Blue Train to get there. When I grow up I shall always follow the sun, won't you, Bill?"

"I don't know," replied the matter-of-fact Bill. "I like the snow and the ice, I'm not sure that I won't go to the North Pole when I grow up. My daddy says that at the North Pole all the clocks tell the same time, is that true, Mr. Pobblethwaite?"

"Well," replied Mr. Pobblethwaite, "your daddy was right in a way, what he should have said, Bill, was that any clock is right at the North Pole, you don't need any special kind of clock there, although it is so far north and so cold."

At that moment Twinks, who had been watching intently a corner of the wood, broke into Mr. Pobblethwaite's discursion on time at the North Pole.

"Bill, do come here," she called, "do come and see what I'm seeing."

Bill followed her pointing finger. The ground which a moment before had been smooth brown earth was being bumped up in different places as if something was moving underneath it.

Then a tiny spike of emerald green poked up out of the soil. Another and another spike appeared till there was a row of them looking for all the world like a line of soldiers' spears.

The row of little spears quivered for a second or two in the sunshine and then, in between them, popped up gleaming white flowers like drops of snow. The buds unfolded and there was a row of snowdrops laughing and giggling to each other like a bunch of schoolgirls.

"Oh, I must talk to them." Twinks ran over and stooped down to the flowers.

"Hallo! you're snowdrops, aren't you?" she said. "Are you glad to be up above ground again?"

"Hallo, Twinks, of course we're delighted to be awake again, but all the same we're always ready for sleep again when the time comes, for we work very, very hard."

Twinks was astonished. "Do you call it working hard, just growing and then——" she nearly said dying, but stopped herself in time, and went on—"sleeping again. I don't call that working at all."

The biggest snowdrop smoothed the green strings of her snowy cap.

"Indeed, then, we work as hard as anyone else. We have to work to get the sunshine to keep alive, we have to work to keep our clothes white and fresh to attract the insects that call on us. We are so busy that we don't even have time to talk much, but that doesn't matter, for if we are fond of each other we understand," and she looked lovingly at her friends clustered around her.

"Yes," chimed in another of the little group, "what do you think would happen to us if we didn't get any insects calling, or if we stopped working just to admire the sun? And," she added shyly, "haven't you seen flowers shutting their eyes when they go to bed?"

Here all the snowdrops lifted their pretty heads to the sunlight as it flickered through the tree tops.

"Our leaves help to make the food that keeps us alive through the dark months when we are sleeping. We have to make and store all our food for the winter, like your Mummy does in her store cupboard. It's you that don't understand what work is." And all the snowdrops pointed their long green fingers at Twinks and chorused: "You don't know what work is."

"Never mind, Twinks." The biggest flower saw that Twinks looked really rather upset. "You'll have to work one day, but don't you forget that we flowers have to work from the very first day we are born."

"I shall never forget what you've told me," Twinks replied. "I think you're all wonderful. But please tell me, when you've finished your work in the sunshine and begin to fade, what happens then?"

For a moment the snowdrops looked puzzled.

"What happens?" they queried. "Oh,

you mean when we begin to feel sleepy. Oh, then we just withdraw into ourselves and go to sleep in Mrs. Nature's underground rooms until we know it's time to come up to earth again, and our spring frocks are ready. What you see left of our outsides up here are just our old cast-off clothes."

Twinks sighed. "There you go again, you know it's time, but how do you know it's time?"

But the snowdrops did not want to talk about time, they had turned their heads and were watching the antics of a small fly in a top-hat who had got on to the end of a blade of grass and was making frantic signs to them that he wanted to get their attention.

The biggest snowdrop, however, did just turn her head again to Twinks and said hurriedly: "We know it's time, because it *is* time."

"It's hopeless—they simply *can't* explain," Bill said to Twinks. "I can't think why you bother about this time affair so much. Why worry about it, they only laugh at you for it."

"I hate being done," replied his sister. "It seems to me that if only we could find out what time is it would explain such a lot. Why do people grow old if all the time they could fiddle about with time and keep young? After all, Mr. P. must be thousands of years old according to us, yet he doesn't behave as if he was old. And the flowers go on and on living through their own and other flowers' lives. I simply must find out how to do the same."

"Well, I think you're silly to bother. Most probably you'd only find that you'd die at once if you mess about with other people's time." And with that parting advice Bill strolled over to where the Time Keeper was deep in conversation with a toad. "Anyway," called Bill over his shoulder, "p'raps you *are* like flowers."

The toad was sitting on top of a stone. It was panting slightly as if it had been running, and as Bill came up, followed by Twinks, they heard it croaking.

"Wait till I've had a bit of sunshine, my lad, then I'll be right as rain. Soon as I feel the sun on my old bones I feel a different creature and ready to start work again."

. "Start work again," Bill repeated wonderingly. "What do you do when you work?"

The toad gasped for breath.

"What do I do? Bless my soul, boy, I've got to get a family first and then, when I come back from the pond, I go back to my hole in the garden and keep down the insects, you know. There's some dratted bad ones too," he added, "I can tell you that, for it's my job to keep 'em down." And he chuckled hoarsely.

"Where's your garden?" asked Twinks.

"Not far from here," the toad answered. "Ask Mr. Pobblethwaite to bring you along to see me one day, he'll bring you, won't you, Mr. P.?"

"Yes, we'll be coming to see Gardener Boffin one day soon," said the Time Keeper, "then my young people can see you at work."

"Look, Mr. Pobblethwaite, do look at those violets." Twinks had wandered a little way away and was watching some purple and white violets growing near the oak tree.

The flowers were turning their pretty heads this way and that. Stroking down their silken petals and waving their arms like any set of chorus girls. They pursed their lips, then smiled invitingly. Nearby were a couple of bees in striped brown coats. They seemed very interested in the flowers and buzzed around them, darting closer and closer. At length one of the bees grew bold and to Twinks' delight it bent down and kissed a violet full on the mouth.

"Now I know why the violets were

perking themselves up," Twinks said. "They wanted the bees to have their honey. What fun it must be for them!"

"Here, Mr. Pobblethwaite, look here," Bill was calling to the Time Keeper, who walked over to where the boy stood by a small wicket gate.

"What is it, Bill?" he asked kindly.

"Look!" Bill pointed to a fragile spider's web that had been delicately hung from one side of the gate to the other in such a way that it must have been snapped off by the first person to open the gate. "That's a silly sort of place to put a web on. Why, it can be broken in a moment."

"It seems silly to you, my boy, your sense of time is quite different from a spider's, you must remember. To that spider a day is the same as fifty years to you, so that if the web lasts for fifty years that is a long time."

"Oh, I see, then it isn't so silly as it seems. I didn't think that spiders would be

so stupid, 'cos they always seem so fright-
fully clever."

"I want to introduce you to some other
very clever insects," said Mr. Pobblethwaite. "Come here, both of you, and
meet one of my beetle friends," and he
went up to a heap of dead leaves where a
big, shiny beetle was busy scratching
about.

As the Time Keeper came up, the beetle
stopped grubbing and turned to face them.
He had a friendly face but at the moment
seemed slightly agitated about something,
for he kept looking about him with bright
twinkling eyes as if on the lookout.

"How are you, Sisyphus?" asked Mr.
Pobblethwaite. "Any luck to-day?"

"I'm fine, thank you, Mr. Time Keeper,"
replied the beetle, "but I'm a bit worried
at the moment for I must get food ready
for my family that's coming along, and
there don't seem much about yet."

"What kind of food are you looking for?" Twinks asked.

"Sisyphus lives on dung," Mr. Pobblethwaite told her. "Look over there, there's Mrs. Sisyphus, she's been lucky enough to find some, now just watch how she manages her store."

Mrs. Sisyphus certainly had remarkable strength. She had collected a big heap of dung from under leaves and twigs. With her nimble legs she had moulded it into a ball many times larger than herself and, having done that, she started rolling this towards the door of her burrow. When Mr. Sisyphus saw what she was up to, he too toddled off to give a helping hand.

"But what on earth does she want all that for?" asked Twinks.

"To feed her coming family," replied Mr. Pobblethwaite. "You see, she will roll that into her burrow and then lay her eggs. Then, when the family hatch out, they'll have plenty of food to keep them going till

[129]

they are big enough to look out for themselves. See, they are far stronger than they look."

"And what do Mr. and Mrs. Sisyphus eat themselves?" Bill said as he watched the beetles struggling with their huge burden.

"Oh, they eat dung balls too, but they see that their family are looked after first," Mr. Pobblethwaite said. "That's true, isn't it, Sisyphus?" and he went to where the two beetles were having a short rest before attacking the ball again.

"That's right, Time Keeper," they panted, "must look after the children first, and then get our own food," and once again they grunted and groaned under their load. "Burying things is easier," said Mrs. S., mopping her forehead, "and what's more I don't have to turn up until I am called." Mr. S. grinned. "Yes," he said, "I have got a lovely rattle."

"Beetles are strange creatures," Mr.

Pobblethwaite said as he sat down again on the fallen tree trunk. "These chaps have relatives that live with ants; in fact they are the ants' pets."

"Ants' pets?" echoed Bill. "What on earth do you mean?"

"Well, they live always near to ants' nests," Mr. Pobblethwaite explained, "and they seem to love the ants very much, for while the ants lick them because they like the taste of the beetles' hairs, the beetles, on the other hand, suck honey from the ants' mouths. Seems a quaint idea, doesn't it? but they all get on very well together."

"I always rather hated beetles," observed Twinks, "but now I see that they're really awfully interesting things."

"The world would certainly be a very much dirtier place without them," remarked Mr. Pobblethwaite, "they are the cleanest things I know. The woods would be in a fearful state but for them. Nature says that she doesn't know what she would do without them."

"Mr. Pobblethwaite, shall we see the Red Admiral again?" Twinks said. "I would like to because he was such a funny little creature, and you did say we'd meet him again."

"So you shall, my dear, so you shall," Mr. Pobblethwaite said. "But not quite yet, it's too early for him to be out and about. He won't wake up for a month or two yet. And now, bless my soul, how time flies!" He consulted his watch again. "We shall have to be off again on our travels, for it's time to go to see Mr. Boffin's garden."

The Time Keeper rose from the trunk and held out his hands to Bill and Twinks.

He walked with them to the little gate where the spider had spun its web. Opening it, he went through, breaking the web and pulling Bill and Twinks after him. . . .

More Spring

Spring's late this year?
Nonsense, look who's here!
The basket is open and the cuckoo's out!
(Now the flowers can bloom, trees leaf, insects
    buzz, worms wriggle and birds sing because
    that wild, rascally stranger from the Mediter-
    ranean has turned up again!)
Everything can start growing,
Greet the spring with a shout!

"Now then, now then, look where you're stepping, don't you spoil my flowers!"

Bill and Twinks rubbed their eyes. Yes, the spectacles were still there, and Mr. Pobblethwaite had taken a large magnifying glass out of his pocket and was trying to look at a white daisy through it.

For they were in a garden. A beautiful

garden too. Full of flowers and shrubs. And they were standing on a bright green lawn.

They looked about to see who had spoken to them and saw a man wearing a rough straw hat and a green baize apron, bending over a flower bed, tying up one of the plants.

As soon as he saw that Bill and Twinks had spotted him he straightened up and smiled in a kindly way.

"My name is Boffin," he said. "I'm Keeper of the King's Garden. Like your friend Pobblethwaite, only he keeps the King's Time and I keep the King's Garden. That's right, isn't it, Mr. Pobblethwaite?"

The King's Time Keeper gave up staring the daisy out of countenance and came up to the King's Gardener.

"Perfectly right, Boffin," he agreed, "perfectly right. I wonder now if you'd mind showing these young people the gar-

AMY·LOW·

CUCKOO TIME

Without beetles, birds, worms and spiders, the world could never be kept clean or the earth made to grow food and flowers

den, and telling them something about the flowers and insects in it? They're only down here for a second or two."

Gardener Boffin grinned amicably. "Well, I think I can spare them a second, Mr. P.," and he held out a gnarled brown hand to Twinks and Bill. "I must say that there's plenty to do now spring has come round again. We're all hard workers in these parts, you know."

Twinks looked up inquiringly. "Is it really true that flowers work hard? They've told us that they do, but we think that just growing can't be a very hard job. I don't feel I'm working just because I'm growing."

Gardener Boffin stooped to tie up a daffodil to a stick with a piece of bass.

"Of course flowers work," he replied, "they have to. If they didn't they couldn't make use of the sunshine and they would just fade away and have no life to go on again next season. You work very hard, don't you, little lady?" and he turned to an elegant bluebell growing close by.

The bluebell rang all her bells in a silvery chime.

"How silly mortals are, Gardener, how *very* silly. We work, but we love our work, so it's play as well." Tinkle, tinkle, tinkle, and the flower went off into peals of laughter.

Gardener Boffin laughed too. A deep, jolly laugh that made you feel happy and contented.

"Flowers have a lot of patience," he added. "Look here," he pointed to a crazy paving-stone from under which a pink convolvulus had forced its way out into the open. "Think how hard Convolvulus must have worked to force her way into the sunlight. She pushed and wriggled and heaved with all her might and main till at last she got through."

"Yes, that is wonderful," Bill said. "Somehow we never thought of things like that before. I just took flowers for granted, they seemed to come up and die down every year and that's all they did. Do they do other things as well as working to grow?"

"They invent," said Mr. Boffin rather mysteriously. "Flowers have invented heaps of things that human beings use now. Like insects too," he continued.

"Invent! whatever do they invent?" Twinks asked.

Gardener Boffin scratched his head. Then he pointed to some lily of the valley blossoms.

"See those flowers, well, their bells are fine sound reflectors, though *you* couldn't hear the sounds they reflect. All the same, their bell shape has been copied for thousands of the instruments used by mortals, especially in picture shows. Then there's Sundew," and he showed them a small, insignificant-looking flower set in a rosette of green leaves. "Sundew traps insects for food. Better than any mouse trap you can produce. And Lords and Ladies, the kind that live in hedges, trap flies too and eat them, so that they may grow strong and able to produce fresh seeds for next year.

Insects too," he went on, stroking the velvet coat of a bee that had settled on his shoulder, "have taught mortals many things: There are some that know so much about putting to sleep that they are able to stab a caterpillar in the right place so that it goes fast asleep, and they keep it alive till they want it to feed their children with."

"You may not believe me," he added solemnly, taking up a trowel and pointing it at Bill, "but if flowers went on long enough they would design every picture in the world that had ever been painted."

"What about weeds," Twinks asked, "are weeds bad flowers because no one seems to want them in their gardens at any rate?"

"Weeds, weeds, tut, tut, there are no such things as weeds, Gardener Boffin answered. "Just because a flower comes up in the wrong place you call it a weed. Weeds are beautiful in their way, just as flowers are. Dandelions are wonderful, ragwort is magnificent. Why despise flowers that only grow in a garden. In the King's Garden," added Boffin proudly, "there is every kind of flower in the world."

Indeed, as they looked about, Bill and Twinks thought they had never seen so many or such beautiful flowers.

"All you have to do if you want any special flower is just to think of it," Boffin told them.

"Oh, please let me see a blue poppy," cried Twinks, and lo and behold in the bed in front of her swayed a beautiful blue flower.

"Where did you come from, blue poppy?" asked Twinks. "I've heard my Uncle talk about you and say that you come from a land very far away where some of the most wonderful flowers in the world grow."

"Yes, that's right." The blue poppy fingered her billowy petals and pirouetted on one slender green leg. "I came from Tibet, from the mountains."

"But how did you get here?" asked Bill. "Surely you did not fly over like the birds do?"

"Fly! of course not! I was brought back while I was asleep by an explorer. He thought I was so beautiful that he wanted me to brighten up his own garden. So here I am; but," the poppy added hastily, "my brothers and sisters are still in Tibet although now I have quite a lot of friends over here."

Here Gardener Boffin interposed: "Blue Poppy means that when her seeds were resting they were brought back here by a very clever gardener who made a corner of his garden ready for them to grow in when they woke up. You see, flowers take a lot of trouble over their appearance, and compared to insects they live very slowly. Some of them take a hundred years to produce one beautiful bloom and then fall asleep for another century before they finish work again. It's just a question of time. Flowers take a lot of trouble over their appearance," he went on, "and compared to insects they live very very slowly. It's just a question of time."

Twinks gave a deep sigh. "I knew we would come to time again," she said. "We've been told that time is really only change, what else can you tell us about it?"

The Gardener chuckled, winked portentously at Mr. Pobblethwaite, and then scratched his forehead with a tanned forefinger.

"Well, we all live at different rates," he told Twinks, "and when we're sleeping time plays us queer tricks. You and Bill may dream you've swum in the sea, climbed a mountain or taken a ten-mile walk all in the space of a second, while the blue poppy may sleep for six months and only think that she has let a bee call on her once. What is a lifetime to the flower in my garden is only a few hours of your much slower life, and to the oak tree, who watches centuries go past, it is no more than a second of *his* life."

While the Gardener was speaking, Bill watched some white daisies smoothing out their frilled caps and green skirts.

"I believe that flowers are just as conceited as girls," he remarked, rather contemptuously. "All they seem to care about is to attract attention."

"They enjoy dressing up," Gardener Boffin said. "Sometimes they imitate the clothes of flies or other insects that visit them. There are orchids that look just like flies and bees. And some white flowers only use scent at night so as to be different to their friends and attract night flying insects. Some shine too with a strange glow for the same reason. They are just like girls, always wanting to do one better than the others!" Here the Gardener gave a side-long glance at Twinks.

"But everything seems to be doing things at different times," Twinks said. "There doesn't seem to be any kind of settledness."

"Time is precious to everything, just the same," the Gardener told her. "It moves just as quickly for the snail that crawls slowly along as for the swallow that darts by in a flash. Speed and time are nothing in nature. You saw how the ivy attacked the oak tree. In nature it would appear to take more than your lifetime probably, yet you can see it happen in a few seconds by looking through your magic glasses. And," he added sagely, "you can see it happen on a high-speed picture when you get home again."

"I think it's too mysterious for words," Twinks said. "I suppose if I could speed myself up I should be an old lady before I was properly grown up, and I should hate that."

At that moment she heard Mr. Pobble-thwaite call her and, turning, she found that personage (she always thought of him as a personage) in animated conversation with a thrush that was hopping about on the King's lawn.

As she and Bill walked nearer the thrush nodded to them in a solemn manner, and Twinks, not knowing quite what to say, inclined her head in an equally grave salute.

"I was just having a chat about early worms," Mr. Pobblethwaite said. "Did you know that the thrush could hear when worms are moving under the ground?"

"Certainly, I can," the thrush replied, "and if the lad and lassie will bend their heads down and listen they will hear them too."

Twinks and Bill bent their heads towards the spot where the thrush was hopping. They heard the most deafening sounds as if, under the soil, some giant drill was moving backwards and forwards, and beneath their feet they could feel a strong vibration of the ground.

"Is that simply fearful noise worms?" they cried quickly stepping backwards to where Mr. Pobblethwaite was watching their discomfiture.

The thrush smiled rather scornfully.

"That noise is worms," it answered.

"That noise is worms," repeated Bill and Twinks. "But we can't hear it now. How can such small things as worms make such a row, how can they?"

"I just let you hear it for a moment," said the thrush. "It does not sound so bad to me, but now you know how I know when the early worm is about," and with that parting shot the bird hopped away, laughing to itself.

"No wonder the worms were nervous about the birds," Bill remarked. "I'm glad I can't hear like a thrush, why, I should be quite deaf in a few seconds. Just fancy, Twinks, what it would be like to hear moles digging."

"Yes, it would be pretty awful," Twinks agreed. "Why, where has Mr. Pobblethwaite gone to?" and she pointed to where the Time Keeper was bending over something set up in the grass.

"Why, it's a sundial," Bill said when they got up to Mr. Pobblethwaite. And sure enough he was gravely comparing the sundial with his own watch.

"Is it right?" asked Twinks.

"Oh, yes, quite correct," Mr. P. told her. "It's one of the best time tellers I know because it takes no notice of what the insects and flowers do with their time, *it* tells the sun's time and it is the sun that speeds up or slows down the time of nearly everything in the garden."

"But I don't understand that; what do you mean?" Twinks stopped pirouetting on one foot and became inquiring again.

"Well, my dear, the sun shines and all the flowers grow quickly and the insects lay their eggs and everything goes along well. Then the sun goes in for weeks on end and all garden life slows down; that's what I mean. And you and Bill may be affected too, because little sun means not so good vegetables for you to eat so that in the long run even your time is altered too."

Twinks shook her curly head.

"You are very clever, Mr. Pobble-thwaite, you seem to know about everything," she told him. "Even the insects and flowers seem to be much cleverer than we are."

Gardener Boffin, who had just come up with his arms full of sticks and rolls of bass, smiled at Twinks' vehemence.

"Perhaps it is that flowers and insects are so painstaking," he said. "Have you ever heard of Cigale?"

"Cigale. What's Cigale?"

"Cigale is an insect that lives in a long twisting burrow under the ground. It digs out first a little parlour, then it scratches an underground passage from the parlour right up to the surface of the ground and it lives in this kind of underworld observatory, taking note of what kind of weather it is upstairs so that when its time comes it won't go out till the weather is suitable. And to keep everything shipshape, Cigale plasters the walls of its little home with the earth that it digs up."

"But how does it know when the weather is right?" asked Bill.

"Quite simple," replied Boffin. "It leaves a thin film of earth across the top of the passage so that it can just pop up now and then and see what is happening. Then, when a really fine day comes, Cigale breaks through the 'window door' and crawls out into the sunshine. It is a patient creature, something like the locust that takes four years underground preparing to be a beautiful lady."

The gardener then began to tie up some of his flowers, and Twinks heard him scolding a tulip for opening too soon, and telling one of the primroses not to be a naughty girl.

"Twinks!" Bill called her across the

garden. "Let's go down to the pond and see if there are any tadpoles." By this time the Time Keeper had also moved away and was sitting on a wooden bench under a may tree talking earnestly to a couple of beetles.

Twinks ran over to Bill and they crossed the green lawn to the big pond at the bottom of the garden.

By the side of the water squatted a number of frogs and toads apparently watching strings and masses of jelly-like looking stuff which floated on the top of the water.

"What do you think they are doing?" Twinks whispered to Bill.

"Watching their children being born."

"Their children being born," repeated Twinks. "I can't see any little frogs or toads. What do you mean?"

"There they are, in that jelly stuff—you look."

And as they watched through their

magic spectacles they saw a strange scene unfolding before them.

In the centre of each spot of jelly was a tiny black speck. They saw these specks grow larger and thicker till the jelly was all absorbed and they could distinguish the dark heads of tiny tadpoles. Then they saw eyes forming and mouths opening. Till from the heads grew out small waving tails, and the black speck almost magically became a tiny swimmer. In a trice it seemed, the water was full of small creatures darting about wildly from one side of the pond to the other.

To this amazing transformation the tadpoles' parents were completely indifferent.

Twinks and Bill heard one fat toad say to another:

"Well, my dear, so-long for this year. Now we'd best be getting back to the garden, there's plenty of work there waiting for us to do. See you again next spring."

And without so much as another look at his offspring, the old toad had set his head for home again.

"Gracious goodness, they're pretty casual, aren't they?" Bill remarked. "They don't seem to care a rap about their children once they are born."

"I think it's jolly sensible," Twinks told him, "it teaches the young ones to be independent and look after themselves. Besides, how on earth could they keep an eye on hundreds of children. I think the whole affair is rather well thought out."

And with that parting shot Twinks started after Mr. Pobblethwaite, who was beckoning them from the other side of the garden.

She found the Time Keeper standing on a patch of grass turf with his watch in his hand. When she came up to him he looked up.

"How do you like Boffin's flower clock?" he asked.

"Flower clock! what's that?" Twinks could only see the watch in Mr. Pobblethwaite's hand.

"There in front of you is the clock." Mr. Pobblethwaite put out his hand and pointed to the stretch of grass.

"Oh," Twinks voice rose. "Why, it looks like a clock all made of flowers. It's lovely. Bill, Bill, come here quick, there's a clock of flowers. Do look."

On the soft green grass was the face of an enormous clock, but the time divisions were marked by different masses of flowers, growing closely packed together and, as far as could be seen, only in bud. In the middle of this floral clock, instead of a long and short hand there was a slender ash sapling.

"But how does it tell time?" Bill asked as he came up. "It looks pretty, but I can't for the life of me see how you tell what time it is."

"Quite easy, my boy, quite easy." Gardener Boffin had come up behind them and was smiling at their curiosity.

"Each time division is filled with certain flowers that open and shut at certain times of the day. All you need do is see which flowers are out and then you know the time. I'll try to explain.

He pointed to the bright yellow flower buds of the division that looked like twenty minutes past the hour on an ordinary clock, and waved his hand. At once the tiny gold heads opened one after the other till the section was a vivid shimmering mass.

"Goats-beard," he told them. "They always open first of all the flowers."

He waved his hand again over the clock and the next lot of dandelion opened out at five o'clock. One by one Gardener Boffin showed his visitors how his flower clock told the time. Seven o'clock for the centaury's pink blossoms, eight for the white waterlily, nine for the sky-blue speedwell, and ten for the scarlet pimpernel.

Twinks sighed as he watched the little flowers open and shut at the wave of their Gardener's hand. "It's all so wonderful," she said. "I suppose that really it's the sun that tells them when it is time to open and shut."

"Yes, that's it," replied Boffin. "Just a matter of knowing when it's time for them to start work."

"But what happens if the sun isn't shining, do the flowers still go on sleeping, or do they wake up just the same?"

"Oh, they wake up just the same," replied Boffin. "You see, time is a matter of rhythm, you can't stop it just because the sun doesn't shine. The sun helps the flowers to wake up, but the rhythm of life never stops, never. Everything in the world first came out of the sea and the tides, the rhythm of the waters is something that is part of every living thing." Boffin stooped to the clock face and smoothed out the crumpled petals of a centaury flower.

"Rhythm — that's something new," Twinks said. "Are there rhythm clocks then, and is it rhythm that makes us hungry or tired? Are time and rhythm the same thing? Do moon's times and tides all go together and do flowers like the moon too?"

Before Gardener Boffin had answered all this, Mr. Pobblethwaite had cut in. . . .

"My goodness," he said, "spring is going and I have to visit the King's Observatory in two ticks. Come, my dears." He turned to Bill and Twinks. "Shut your eyes tight, count ten, and then open them again. Good-bye, Boffin, see you again next year."

Bill and Twinks shut their eyes tightly. "Good-bye, Mr. Boffin, and thank you," they called. . . . One, two, three, four, five, six, seven, eight, nine, TEN. . . .

Lots More Spring

If it was time for dinner for me
And time for supper for you,
I don't see how we could meet for tea
However we tried, do you?

But if time is only just what we think
Wherever we happen to be,
We could choose what we wanted to eat
  and drink
And call it our din-sup-tea!

"AND what new wonders have you to show us to-day, Professor? These young friends of mine are trying to get a working idea of time, perhaps you can help them?"

At the sound of Mr. Pobblethwaite's voice Twinks and Bill opened their eyes.

New wonders indeed! It seemed to them that in the strange world into which they had strayed, wonders would never cease!

The happy, flower-filled garden and Mr. Boffin had completely disappeared. They were in a large circular room roofed by a glass dome and with walls of thick opaque glass. Through the dome stuck the nose of a huge telescope, the other end of which was fixed in the centre of the room, surrounded by dozens of wheels and handles.

By this gigantic instrument stood Mr. Pobblethwaite and an untidy-looking old man with long white whiskers almost hiding the rest of his face. This strange individual had one hand resting lovingly on the side of the telescope as if it was some dearly-loved child, and his beady eyes twinkling through a pair of horn-rimmed spectacles surveyed Bill and Twinks as if they were two new stars that had just swum into view.

THE EARLY BIRD

Birds can hear insects moving and flowers too have taught
other living things to make use of Nature's help, how to be
comfortable, even how to make pictures

Mr. Pobblethwaite introduced them with a wave of his hand.

"This is Professor Zodiacus, the King's

Astronomer," he explained. "You can ask him anything you want to know."

The queer-looking Professor gave a quick little bow, first to Twinks and then to Bill.

"Only too glad to meet any friends of the Time Keeper's," he said. "My telescope is the most wonderful telescope in the sky, and you can see all the marvellous things you want to through it."

"In the sky!" Twinks caught her breath. "Are we in the sky; you don't mean that we are really up in the sky now?" She clutched at Bill's arm as if to reassure herself that her feet were still on the ground.

Mr. Pobblethwaite gave a funny little smile.

"No need to be afraid, but we are in the sky. The Royal Observatory is up in the middle of the Milky Way. It's easier to see the stars from the sky than the earth. The King's Astronomer has to keep an eye on them and see that everything goes along all right. Otherwise some of the new stars might be shooting off in all the wrong directions."

"But . . . but . . ." put in Bill. "How'll we ever get home again?"

"Never fear, my boy, we'll get you home again safely, and in good time for tea, don't worry your head about that," and the Professor echoed Mr. Pobblethwaite's words . . . "We'll get you home again all right," as he polished the eyepiece of the telescope with his coat sleeve.

"I suppose it's all right," Twinks murmured to Bill, "anyhow we're here now so do let's see all we can."

"What would you like to see first?" asked the Professor, bending to adjust the giant lens as he spoke.

Twinks laughed, she suddenly had an idea. "We can't see time through your telescope, can we?" she asked. "I always feel frightened when I look through a telescope. I'm afraid I shall see something so bright and extraordinary that I shan't be able to bear it."

The Professor stopped polishing the lens and pushed his spectacles up on top of his mop of white hair.

"I will show you something that will astonish you, but it won't frighten you," he replied. "But time . . . time is so many things . . . time is change and hard and soft, and time is rhythm. Still, perhaps I can show you a little bit of what time really is." And he stooped down again and began to twist and turn the little knobs round the lenses.

Twinks noticed that outside the heavy glass windows of the observatory the sky seemed dark, like night, but inside the room, although there was no sign of any lamps, all was light, almost as if the sun was shining. It was very strange standing there in what appeared to be just one room hung up in the sky like a star with just nothing but space all round them. Twinks shivered, the idea of nothing but space rather frightened her.

Then Bill nudged her. "Look," he said, "there are all sorts of queer lights outside; I wish we could open one of the windows," and as he spoke a brilliant rocket-like thing shot across the darkness and then disappeared.

"Now, my dears," the voice of the Professor broke in, "you may look through the telescope, there is room for you both to look together. Come and kneel down here," and he showed them where to kneel on a soft padded seat just under the giant lens.

"First of all, take a look at the sky," he said, and Twinks and Bill peered up through the telescope.

It seemed like looking at a soft mass of deep blue-black gauze studded with glittering stones that moved about as they gazed at them.

The Professor then began to turn more knobs furiously.

"This time I will show you a star," he said, and the dark sky grew brighter and brighter and the stones bigger and bigger.

Twinks caught at Bill's hand. Isn't it wonderful!" she cried. "I've never seen such a glorious kind of light. What is it, please, Professor?"

"Starlight," replied the King's Astronomer, "and what you're seeing now began in William the Conqueror's time. It has taken all those years to get as far as this; what do you think of that?" And he rubbed his hands together delightedly and nodded his head to Mr. Pobblethwaite.

Bill looked puzzled. "Do you mean to say that the light that's in those stars now won't be seen till my great, great, great, great grandchildren have great, great, great grandchildren of their own?"

"Something like that, my boy," answered the Professor. "If you were up in that star now and could see down to what you call the earth, you'd be watching the Roman chariot races, or looking at Alfred the Great burning the cakes. It's just a matter of time. You could see the ancient savages in their caves behind and the supermen of 1300 A.D. in front. *If* you could manage to put yourself outside time altogether."

"But it's all to do with light as well," put in Twinks. "What is light, is it the same as time?"

The Professor grinned. "Light, my child, is only a feeling, a sensation. It only exists in your mind really. If the sun was green you'd call white a glaring colour. What you think is light has no more existence outside your mind than the smell of an onion."

"I don't understand," Twinks said. "When I turn off a light it's dark, and when I turn it on again I can see. How do you explain that?"

"If you drop a brick on your toe it hurts, doesn't it?" rejoined the Professor. "But you wouldn't say you had dropped the pain, would you? What you call light might just as well make a flower open, which it does, or take a photograph. Besides," he added, "there are lots of lights and you can't see by all of them . . . some only work on insects' or flowers' eyes."

"Do the people on the stars see us down here?" Bill asked.

"If there are any," the Professor laughed. "But they won't see you and Twinks anyhow, as I've just told you. They'll be looking at cave men and dinosaurs. Don't forget," he whispered, "you are only a real person because you live on your earth."

Twinks took a deep breath. "Professor, what *is* time?"

"Bless my soul, there she goes again," roared Mr. Pobblethwaite. "You tell her, Professor, or she'll never be satisfied."

"Time," the Professor grunted. "Time is just everything changing. If we did not notice that things had changed we should not know what time had passed. Don't you let Mr. Pobblethwaite make you believe that his clocks measure time. They don't. They only record its passing. I said just now that rhythm marks time too. We can't live without rhythm. To the creatures that live in the sea rhythm is time. Take some of them out of the water and keep them on land in tanks and they still live according to the tune of the sea. So do you if you did but know it."

Twinks and Bill shook their heads. It all sounded so easy but it was so mixed up, they thought. First it was change, now it was rhythm . . . or even both together.

They turned again to the telescope.

"Look again," said the Professor. "Watch the dance of the atoms."

Again they peered up through the giant instrument, while the King's Time Keeper, spreading his handkerchief over his rubicund face, lay down on a sofa to have a nap.

For a moment everything seemed to swim before their eyes. Then the misty surface cleared and they saw what looked like miniature globes turning and whirling before them. These little globes were not unlike the tadpoles they had seen hatch out in the pond in the King's Garden.

They seemed to dance closer and closer to each other till, suddenly, they touched, spun wildly away again, then merged closer and closer till they melted in one mass that looked at first like an enormous drop of water.

"What is it all about?" Bill asked.

"You've just almost seen an atom of hydrogen and two atoms of oxygen come together and turn into an atom of water," the Professor told him. "Atoms may be inhabited, you know, but of course, no one has yet been able to make a telescope powerful enough to distinguish the creatures who live on them. I've got a new telescope using a new kind of light being made now. A cosmicscope," he said almost to himself.

"It's fearfully interesting," said Twinks. "I wish you would show us a comet, Professor. Mother told me that she saw one when she was young and that it started in 1066 and some people thought it would burn us all up if it came too close. What is a comet exactly, Professor?"

Instead of answering at once, the Professor went solemnly to a bookcase in one corner of the observatory and took from it a heavy volume which he opened. He ran his wrinkled finger down one page, and stopped at a line.

"Yes, I think I can just do it," he said to himself. "What's o'clock?" and he went over to a table where there lay a small saucer filled with a mass of something that looked like glue.

He touched the mass with his finger. It

[169]

was soft and quivered slightly under his prodding.

"It's all right, plenty of time. Think I can just catch it."

"Catch what? Do tell us what you are doing, please."

"Catch the comet, of course," answered the Professor testily. "That's one of my ways of telling the time. That stuff on the plate. If it's hard I know I've not got much time and if it's soft I have plenty. Time is really only hard and soft, you know," he added, "like water when you dive in too quickly. When the atoms change speed they often harden and their time is hurrying on. But if they just meander about in big circles and keep soft, then time is fairly slow and there is plenty to spare." Here the Professor gave another look at the stuff on the plate.

"There's a comet due in two ticks," he said agitatedly. "Be ready now."

Bill and Twinks looked eagerly through

the great telescope and, as they watched, across the giant lens spread a faint glow which grew brighter and brighter till it suddenly concentrated into a streak of brilliant light that seemed to split the glass. A vivid flash shot out and then was gone.

"Is that all?" Twinks was disappointed. She didn't know exactly what she had hoped to see, but it was something more than a flash, she felt sure.

"Well, what did you expect?" grumbled the Professor. "Just gas, that's all a comet is, just gas. And yet they behave as if they were the cat's whiskers. Still, I must say they do travel, they certainly do travel," and muttering to himself he began again to polish the sides of his beloved instrument with a silk handkerchief.

Twinks got up from looking through the telescope and wandered away to where Mr. Pobblethwaite was peacefully sleeping on the sofa, but Bill had something to say to the Professor.

"It's funny, isn't it?" he began rather diffidently, "how some things are so small, like fleas, and others so awfully big, like elephants. But if we look at them through a telescope, the little things look as big as the big things look when we don't look at them through a telescope. What I can't understand is what is their real size?"

The Professor stopped his polishing.

"Pooh," he said to Bill, "nature does not bother much about size. What is size, anyway? To a germ a butterfly looks like a bomber, but to an atom a germ is as big as a battleship, and a human being as vast as a continent. Don't you see, my boy," he went on solemnly, "that if everything was twenty times as big you wouldn't see any difference. Everything would look just the same!" And with that the Professor went back to his polishing.

Twinks, by this time finding that Mr. Pobblethwaite showed no signs of waking up, had come back to the Professor again.

"I wish we could see the sun," she said, "but I suppose it would be so awfully bright that it would dazzle us too much."

The Professor almost snorted.

He went to one of the big windows and pointed to a twinkling star that seemed to be hanging just outside.

"That's the sun," he said.

"The sun!" Twinks was staggered. "That little star the sun!"

"Yes," answered the Professor, "and what's more, it's about 93 million miles away from where you were just now, and that other little star nearby is the earth!"

"But we were on the earth before we came up here," put in Bill. "However can we get back again? It makes me giddy to think about it. Let's talk of something else."

A grunt from Mr. Pobblethwaite told them that the King's Time Keeper had woken up.

"You've been asleep quite a long time,"

remarked Twinks, as he got up from the couch and pulled out his watch.

"I've been asleep exactly one tick," retorted Mr. Pobblethwaite, "and in that time I travelled all round the sun and back."

"But you only thought you did," Bill said. "You didn't really travel round the sun."

Mr. Pobblethwaite drew his handkerchief out of his coat pocket and began brushing his coat free of dust.

"I certainly did go to the sun," he replied. "That's the best of dreams, you can live through a lifetime in a second and squash in a thousand different actions without the slightest trouble."

Here the Professor broke into the conversation. "I don't wish to rush you, my friends," he said, "but it's getting on for summer-time, and if you don't hurry you'll find that you've lost a lot of very precious time."

Mr. Pobblethwaite tucked away his handkerchief and turned to Bill and Twinks.

"Now," he told them, "I want some of that time you lost years ago. Shut your eyes, count twenty, and then open them again. One, two, three . . ."

Summer

In a dream
You can run round the world,
You can climb
The Alps in a trice,
You can dive to the bottom of the sea,
Or go to the moon
In a balloon.
There is no time
In a dream.
Time is just in your head
And when you dream
It isn't dead!

THEY stood on the top of a little hill. The
sun shone brightly, the air was warm. Below them stretched a grassy flower-decked
meadow, on one side lay a shady wood, on
the other a river wound its way in and out

[176]

THE PARACHUTES
*Many seeds use parachutes to find good homes. Nothing is
really new under the sun*

of fields right up to a hazy blue in the distance.

"That's quick travelling, isn't it?" Bill looked round him as if afraid that at any minute he might be swept off somewhere else. . . . He felt quite hot.

"Yes, not bad going," remarked Mr. Pobblethwaite. "You'd get used to these sudden changes if you lived for long like we do. As I've said before, time is really just fast and slow. It's summer-time now and I've brought you here to see the great Summer Pageant. Every season it's held. I think you'll be interested."

"Pageant of what?" Twinks always liked to know exactly what she was supposed to be seeing, in case she might miss anything.

"Oh, everything," replied Mr. Pobblethwaite vaguely, waving one hand. "I can't tell you the whole lot, but you'll see soon for yourself." He then proceeded to open his umbrella which he planted in the ground by the handle, thus making a multi-coloured tent under which he sat himself comfortably cross-legged on the grass.

"It's a fine sight, a very fine sight," said a wheezy voice in Twinks' ear. She looked round quickly and saw at her side a large beetle leaning on a spade and panting as if it had been hurrying.

"How on earth did you come here?" she asked.

"Come here? come here? I like that, I do," grumbled the creature. "That's a good 'un, that is. This is my beat, and I'll ask you, young miss, what *you* are doing 'ere on Pageant Day without a ticket?"

"It's all right, Scraper," interrupted the Time Keeper, lazily opening one eye. "These are friends of mine just down from the Observatory. They've come to see the Pageant."

"Sorry, Mr. Time Keeper, I'm sure I never saw *you*, sir," grumbled the beetle.

[179]

"But we get so many of these gate crashers that I've been put on a special beat to scare 'em away."

"What exactly is this Pageant?" Bill asked, eyeing the beetle with interest. He couldn't quite see why it had to have a spade even if it was on its beat.

"Well, it's just a show of all the creatures and flowers," said the beetle. "This is a rare good place to see it from too. Listen! the trumpets are sounding up now."

Across the meadow lying so green and peaceful before them sounded the clear notes of trumpets, and at the far end appeared two trumpeters mounted on magnificent white horses, with red and blue saddles.

"Oh, Bill, this is going to be marvellous," cried Twinks, clapping her hands excitedly. And I do believe that Mr. P. is asleep."

"Oh no, I'm not, my child, no I'm not." The Time Keeper got up from his seat under the umbrella and joined Twinks and Bill and the beetle where they stood looking down at the Pageant below.

"Most mortals can't see the Pageant properly as they haven't any magic spectacles, but you and Bill will be able to see and hear."

"See and hear, can't you smell too?" inquired someone gently in a voice that sounded something between a sigh and a soft breeze. "And even if you can't smell you ought to be able to touch. Fancy only being able to see and hear. . . ." And the voice died away altogether.

Twinks and Bill both started, for as far as they could see there was no one else near them but the beetle and Mr. Pobblethwaite.

"When it comes to the shooting I should take cover if I were you. My great, great, great grandmother says that when her great, great great grandfather's great grandfather was watching the Pageant he was shot by a gorse-gun and had a hole through him for always and always."

"Who are you? Where are you?" Twinks felt rather annoyed, it was so silly just listening to a voice with nobody attached to it.

Then she suddenly felt something touch her ankle and she looked down. On the grass stood a slender creature in green tights. So slim, in fact, that it looked almost like a green shadow.

"I'm grass, green grass," murmured the voice. "Don't you know me? I'll make myself tall so that you can see me better." And in a trice the grass had grown up as tall as Twinks' shoulder and she found herself looking into the green eyes of a blade of grass.

"Do you mean to say that you can make yourself grow tall just when you like?"

"Well, I'm growing all the time." The grass put out a green finger and stroked Twinks' cheek gently. "Growing is just a matter of time, and of course time is what we make it, dear. But look, here comes the Royal Messenger to announce the Pageant. And Grass pointed out across the meadow where a great concourse of creatures and flowers had gathered.

Across the grass stalked a truly magnificent figure wearing a heavy black velvet cloak slashed with scarlet and white. In the centre of the meadow it struck an attitude of pride and in a loud voice that echoed up to the hilltops announced that the Pageant would start with a display by the flowers of the latest fashions.

There was a low platform set near the middle of the meadow and across this walked the flower mannequins one by one.

There were irises in rich royal purple dresses; poppies wearing the scarlet of the royal soldiers. Gold and white Madonna lilies displayed bridal robes and veils; pink and yellow roses trailed their silken skirts.

"They are beautiful," Twinks said to the Time Keeper who was trying to see more of the mannequins by peering through a pair of binoculars.

. "They know how to blend the finest colours in the world," said Mr. Pobble-thwaite, and they could design all the frocks in the world if they wanted to. There's no new colour, at least what you mortals call new, that hasn't already been invented by the flowers. When a gardener makes a great fuss about growing some new flower or other, he forgets that he has not really done it all, it's the flower that has made the colours. Bees are much more clever than gardeners, because they go to the flowers and between them they make new flowers bloom.

"What I can never understand is how the lovely colours of a flower are all inside the little brown seeds," said Twinks. "How can the rose really come out of a little tight green bud that is half dead all the winter-time?"

"Never half dead, my dear, never," Mr. Pobblethwaite reproved her. "Just asleep, growing all the time, with all the miracle of colour and shape locked up in the seed or the bulb. Then the sun comes and out comes the beauty. Look, now the butter-flies are going to dance."

If the flowers were beautiful, but but-terflies were beautiful too. They flew in a myriad intricate dances, a blaze of colour and grace.

"Pretty good show, what? though I trained them myself." Standing under Mr. Pobblethwaite's umbrella was a dashing figure in black and scarlet, wearing an Admiral's cocked hat and high boots.

"Why, it's the Red Admiral, I do be-lieve," cried Twinks.

"You've altered since we last saw you," Bill said. "I expect you're jolly glad to be out of that chrysalis, aren't you?"

"Shiver my timbers, the young chap is right." The Red Admiral slapped his thigh with his gloved hand. "I like being in the navy and shall spend the rest of my life in it. There's nothing like a life on the ocean wave, yo, heave ho! You'd never think that when I stand on a bridge it bends. Only a little, course," he added hastily, seeing the look of amazement on Bill's face, "but I'm the cat's whiskers in the navy, I can tell you. So long." And with a wave of the hand the Red Admiral had flown away before they could say another word.

"But, surely, he only lives for about two days, doesn't he?" asked Twinks. "He talks as if he lived for years and years and years."

"So he does, so he does," replied Mr. Pobblethwaite. "Can't you *ever* understand this time business, my dear. His two days is just as long to the Red Admiral as your father's sixty years is to him. It's all in how you think it is. You'll meet the Red

Admiral again soon and then he'll be quite different. Now don't bother your head about other people's time for the moment, the mock battle is about to begin."

"I warn you, you'd better take cover when the shooting starts," Grass whispered to Twinks. "You don't want to be shot, do you?"

Twinks and Bill looked across the meadow. At one end yellow-suited little figures were firing gorse guns at another set of figures whose weapons were like rather small hand grenades that exploded with loud pops at intervals.

"Them guns are pretty fierce, I reckon," remarked the beetle who had come up again to watch the fun after a short patrol of the hillside to see that no unauthorized visitor had appeared.

"I've seen and heard some of you mortal folk's guns and there's nothing you've invented that I knows of that we haven't had here first."

"Well, I'm sure that's not quite true."

Twinks could not stand always being told how silly mortals were. "You haven't got any tanks, or armour or anything like our army has, so there."

"There you'm quite wrong, Missy," the beetle said solemnly. "Look at our tanks." It pointed below where on the grass were lined rows of green tanks that had just begun to move in a lumbering way across the meadow. "Them's our tanks," went on the beetle. "You may call 'em caterpillars, but them's the first tanks, and just as good as yours. And what about the snail's armour, and the turtle's and the hedgehog's prickles. If someone runs after you, little Miss, you can't do nothin' but run away, but if you had hairs like the nettle you'd be able to keep 'em off. As for that there camooflage, as you call it, we'm better at that than you be, Missy. Lots of butterflies and birds and animals, for that matter, can make themselves invisible."

"I don't believe it," put in Bill. "I don't

know any living creature that can make themselves invisible. You tell us some."

"That's easy," said the beetle. "You can't see white hares in the snow, or Golden-Eight moths on trees, because they look like leaves, or a grey donkey in a field at twilight, or an arrow-worm in the sea or a curlew on its nest."

"Yes, I'm afraid you're wrong about that," said Mr. Pobblethwaite. "The plants and creatures taught mortals all they think they invented for themselves. . . . Why, *lots* of water people swim with jets!"

"And you can't even find me now."

Twinks turned sharply round. Grass had disappeared. All round her was grass, but no sign of the slender green grass who had spoken.

Twinks laughed. "Yes, I'm wrong," she replied. "You see, we don't realize how clever all nature is and no one seems to bother to teach us about these sort of interesting things at school."

At that moment Mr. Pobblethwaite interrupted the argument by calling to them to come and see paratroops.

Hundreds of tiny white parachutes were sailing in the air and figures could be seen attached to them. One or two seemed to be floating in the direction of the hill-top and they could see distinctly the silken balloon tops and the cords underneath attached to the wearers.

Plomp, down came one quite close to where Twinks and Bill were standing. The parachutist quickly untwined the cords and stepped free.

"Did that fairly well; there's a prize we're after and I think we did our show a bit quicker than the thistle group."

"What group do you belong to?" Bill was fingering the silken parachute that felt like gossamer to the touch.

"We're the dandelions," the parachutist answered. "But there is not much breeze to-day and we had a bit of difficulty in getting off."

"I've thought of one thing that we've got and you haven't," Twinks said to the beetle, "that's aeroplanes."

"Aeroplanes," broke in the dandelion parachutist. "We can travel as well as you mortals. What about the winged seeds of sycamores or elms, or the spiders that sail from place to place on their webs? And we don't want aeroplanes to carry us about because we have birds that carry seeds from continent to continent. Why, it was only by watching birds that mortals were able to make aeroplanes. And they're not half so good as birds, anyhow." He gave a twitch to his yellow overalls.

"I think I'd better be getting back again to the show." And without even so much as a good-bye the dandelion strode away down the hill-side, leaving his silken parachute in a heap on the grass.

"I do hope he isn't annoyed," Twinks sighed. "I always seem to get involved in arguments, and I always come off worst."

Mr. Pobblethwaite smiled. "Well, my dear, you've a lot to learn," he reminded her. "You forget that nature had been working away for hundreds of thousands of years before *your* ancestors came on the scenes. If you can think of anything that human beings can do that hasn't already been done by flowers or other living creatures, I shall be surprised."

Twinks wrinkled her forehead.

"Yes, I can, at least I think I can," she said. "Flowers and animals, or insects for that matter, can't write books."

"My dear," the Time Keeper looked at her sadly. "If a monkey was to get hold of a typewriter and go on banging away at the keys for years and years and years, in the long run, not at once, but in the very long run, it would write all the books that had ever been written."

"But," cried Bill, interrupting, "we thought of letters and words and writing, didn't we? No other creatures have sense enough to write, or read."

Mr. Pobblethwaite looked slightly startled at this poser. But he was at no loss for an answer.

"Flowers and other creatures don't need to talk, or read or write. They know without being taught. Animals don't go to school much. Instinct tells them what to do and how to do it. Tadpoles don't have to be taught to swim, and flowers know what are the right colours to wear without being told or wasting time talking. Baby spiders make webs like their mother's straight away. And birds can fly after only a few trial trips. No, no," and Mr. Pobblethwaite shook his head. "You can't do a *thing* that we haven't done it before, or do it better now."

"You're wrong!" Bill's tone was triumphant.

"You didn't know anything about wireless, you can't send messages and speak over miles and miles like we can, so there."

The Time Keeper laughed as if he had been told a good joke.

"My boy, you don't know what you are saying," he replied. "Birds and insects have been using the vibrations of air and electricity ever since the world began. Shut up Mrs. Oak Eggar moth in a cage four miles away from her husband and he can tune in to her vibrations and find her with the greatest of ease. Pigeons find their way home by knowing the right turnings. They don't need signposts every few miles as you do when you go far away from home. And there are flies that can't grow or have families so well if they are separated and shut up in boxes with thin sheets of 'wave stoppers' between them. They can't feel the vibrations of their friends so they just fade away."

"I give it up, don't you, Twinks," laughed Bill. "Seems we really are a long way behind you so we'd better stop boasting about how clever we are."

"And now we seem to have been talking so much that the parade is over," said

Twinks, and indeed the meadow below them was rapidly emptying and they watched the flowers and animals trooping off while the insects and birds buzzed and flew about as if unwilling to go home.

Green Grass had dwindled down to its usual size and Twinks heard a very faint voice saying: "I'm going to have a bit of a snooze now."

But the old beetle was still there leaning on his spade.

"Master wants to see you," he said to Mr. Pobblethwaite.

"Yes, I'm just going down to have a word with him now." And Mr. Pobblethwaite began to roll up his umbrella as he spoke.

"The River Keeper wants to have a word with me about something or other." He turned to Bill and Twinks who were still watching the scene in the meadow.

"Come along now, my dears, we can walk down the hill to him. Good-day,

[195]

Scraper." And the Royal Time Keeper started down the hill-side.

"Good-bye, thank you for talking to us." Twinks waved her hand to the beetle, who never even bothered to answer but shut his eyes as if to blot out the sight of anything so stupid as a human being.

"Come on, Bill, let's see who can get to the bottom first," and suiting the action to the word, Twinks ran down the slope after Mr. Pobblethwaite. . . .

More Summer

You cannot catch the fleeting minute
By trying to salt its tail,
It has no love for sugared cakes,
Or Bass's BEST PALE ALE.

The only way to trap the thing
And make it cool its heels,
Is to offer it a deep-sea pie
Of lovely jellied eels!

THE fisherman on the opposite bank took no notice whatever of Mr. Pobblethwaite and his friends. Every now and then he reeled in his line, adjusting the fly, and with a skilful flick of the wrist sent it skimming over the water again. But he was so intent on his sport that he had eyes and ears for nothing else.

"Who is he?" Twinks pulled Mr. Pobblethwaite's sleeve. "Can we go over and talk to him?"

Mr. Pobblethwaite put his hand to his mouth and shouted, his voice echoing down the stream.

"Hi! Can we come over and talk to you? We won't jerk the banks."

This did penetrate the fisherman's brain for he lifted his head and looked keenly round to see who had hailed him. When he caught sight of Mr. Pobblethwaite he grinned.

"Thought it must be you," he called. "Just about your time now. Come along over and have a chat." He began to reel in his line again.

"This way, my dears." Mr. Pobblethwaite led the way along the bank till they came to a small rickety bridge that spanned the stream. In a few seconds they were all three standing at the fisherman's side.

"Good-day to you," said the Time Keeper. He turned to Twinks and Bill.

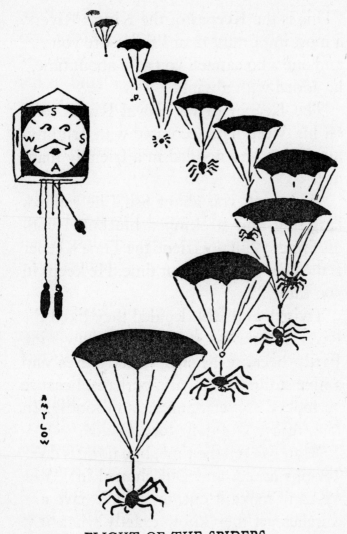

FLIGHT OF THE SPIDERS

*All kinds of things fly in nature. Some insects can hover better
than any airplane*

"This is the Keeper of the King's Rivers, a most important man I do assure you ... and one who can tell you a lot about time," he added with a wink.

The Keeper of the Royal Rivers took off his tweed hat, decorated with brightly-hued flies, and nodded in a friendly manner.

"I can tell you about fish," he replied, laughing and stroking a bluebottle with his finger, "but my friend the Time Keeper is the chap to talk about time. He keeps it, you know."

Twinks and Bill decided they liked the River Keeper as soon as they saw him. Partly because he had twinkly eyes and a nice smile, and partly, perhaps, because he looked so very human and kindly. In fact, rather like their own Daddy.

"Can fish tell the time, like flowers do?" Twinks asked, and Bill chimed in: "Yes, we can't make it out, they don't have any watches yet they know exactly when it is time to do what they have to do. Are fish like that?"

The Keeper of the Royal Rivers who had put on his hat again was fiddling about with his rod. He stopped and looked up at the two eager faces.

"I've never heard of fish that had watches, or clocks for that matter," said he. "But they have a certain kind of sense that tells them when to act. Time's rhythm, you know. There's the rhythm of the tides that tells the sea and river creatures what time it is. All life is rhythm like the tides really. First came the seas and the tides and then out of the water came life with the tide rhythm ready made in its head. To be out of rhythm is to be out of step, out of tune. Just fancy," he patted Twinks' curly head, "what you'd say if you saw roses trying to grow in the middle of a snowstorm. But the rhythm time clocks never go wrong. There's a sea worm that swarms from the rocks into the sea every winter in mid-December just after midnight at high tide. The worms make love to each other then, and after a couple of hours every worm has disappeared again. That's what they were given life to do and they do it at the same time every season. Queer things, time and rhythm," and the River man shook his head. Fish are queer things too," he went on musingly. "Very queer. They can read simple letters and they're sensitive little dears, can't bear the slightest bump. If you were to throw that boulder," and he pointed to a big stone on the bank, "if you threw that into the water they'd have bad headaches for a week afterwards."

"Can fish see us?" Bill asked. "I've often wondered if they could see people when they are fishing, and if that's why they keep down at the bottom."

"Well," answered the River man, "they can see along bent light as it passes from the water to the air, and that's why we fishermen stand back from the bank so as to keep out of sight. But the fish have to be pretty wide awake all the time, because the gulls can spot them like aeroplanes see submarines, and then down they swoop to make a kill. No, it's not an easy life, I can tell you, being a fish, and if one of you mortals come along and take them into artificial water they die almost at once. Why, some are so clever they match their coat to the sands so that no one can see them."

"Do you ever catch anything?" Bill asked curiously because the Keeper seemed to be very unhandy with his rod and line, and there was nothing but a couple of spools in his basket.

"To tell you the truth I don't bother about catching anything," the Keeper told him. "I only watch the fish to see that everything is all right, and sometimes the only way to get them to come to the surface is to float a nice juicy fly before their

[203]

eyes. They generally pop up then, and when they see it's only me they stop for a chat."

"What sort of fly is that?" Twinks pointed to a delicate gauzy-winged insect that was flitting above the surface of the water. "It never seems to stop for a second."

"That's a Mayfly." The Keeper held out his hand and the dainty creature hovered and stayed on his outstretched finger. "You have a crowded life, don't you, my dear?"

"That I do," squeaked the Mayfly. "Why, I have so much work to do that I never even have time to eat. Good-bye, can't stop gossiping any longer," and it darted off to dance with a crowd of other flies in and out of the reeds on the bank.

"Four years the Mayflies live under the water getting ready to come out as a lovely lady or handsome husband," the River Keeper told them. "Then they unfold their wings and dance together through a summer day. Then they lay their eggs in the water and lie down to sleep. They never see their children, but they do their work well, and all in a day too. At least," he added, "you mortals call it a day, but it is as long as your own life to the Mayfly."

"It seems an awful waste of time to be born and die so quickly," Bill said thoughtfully. "They have no time to learn anything, do they?"

"Waste, there's no such thing as waste," retorted the River Keeper. "They waste less of their time than you, I expect! Nothing is lost ever, anywhere, and everything of Nature's is used in some way. Life *never* stops, it only changes."

Suddenly he grabbed Twinks' hand.

"Look, you're in time to see a change take place. See that twig," and he pointed to a thick reed that stuck out of the water, on the end of which was a small bit of what looked like twig.

As Twinks and Bill bent forward they saw the twig crack down the centre and something bright glittered. Then the twig moved and cracked again and from one end stuck out a shiny green head. There was a wriggle, the twig fell to pieces, and there on the tip of the water reed clung a brilliant dragonfly, his wings shimmering in the sunshine.

"How lovely!" said Bill and Twinks together.

"Yes, I am rather gorgeous." The dragonfly lifted up its head haughtily. "But I thought I'd never get out in time, that skin was terribly tough."

"In time?" queried Twinks. "In time for what?"

"Time to do my job, of course," the dragonfly replied pettishly. "What do you think I meant? I've got plenty of flowers to call on and fertilize, *and* I've got to find a wife too," he added, "*and* see that she lays our eggs before the winter. You don't seem to have much work to do," it commented scornfully, "but I must be off. So long." And with a whirr of its painted wings the dragonfly flew away.

"They don't think much of us, do they?" Twinks felt quite squashed. "They make me feel an awful dud," she went on, "for they've all got jobs to do while Bill and I don't seem to be any use at all."

"Don't lose heart," the River Keeper said kindly. "You'll do all right. You're living at a different rate from the insects. If you could see your life speeded up to match theirs you would be born and grow up and get married and have a family like they do in no time. Your time rate is slower, that's all. Now," he went on, "perhaps you'd like a little walk, because I have to attend a meeting of the King's Water Keepers and give a lecture on why shrimps make good mothers."

"But do they?" asked Twinks wonderingly.

The Keeper looked at her. "Very good mothers, as a rule," he replied. "But I've come across some that don't seem to have any maternal sense at all so I thought that if I gave the under-Keeper a bit of advice they might give some of the younger shrimps a talking to when they need it."

Mr. Pobblethwaite brought out his watch. Try as she would, Twinks could never catch a glimpse of its dial, for the Time Keeper took good care to keep it well away from her curious gaze and she could never understand why.

"Yes, I think we have time for a short walk," he said to the River man, "we have got a couple of ticks to spare."

The River Keeper led them along the river bank. He let Bill carry his basket, but kept hold of the rod and line which he held up against his shoulder in military style.

"It's awfully quiet in the water," Bill said as they walked along by the gently rippling stream. "Except for the fish, I can't see anything much in it."

"Bless my soul, boy, are you blind?" Both the River Keeper and the Time Keeper stopped and looked at each other in astonishment.

Bill stopped too and looked down closer at the water.

Something must have happened, he thought, because where it had before seemed clear except for reeds was now a mass of moving creatures. There were flies skimming over the top of the water like skaters on ice; there were queer wheel-shaped masses of jelly moving about; tiny green insects floating in heaps from one side to the other, and tadpole-like things that flicked along by means of threads that they lashed to and fro. It was just like a forest bursting with life.

Bill stood entranced.

"Look, Bill, do look at that thing, it's like an acrobat in a top hat."

Twinks was looking over his shoulder into the water. "Whatever is it?"

The River man looked too and then laughed. "That's Hydra," he said, putting his hand into the water and letting a tiny creature climb out on to his palm. "Meet Bill and Twinks, Hydra, tell them the latest news from the river."

Twinks thought she had never seen such a queer little creature before. At close quarters it looked like a half inch bit of string, the head part being frayed into strands like hair sticking up on end. But when she looked closer she saw that these straggly ends really fringed Hydra's mouth. What made it more difficult was that the creature kept on getting first bigger and then suddenly dwindling down into a knob so that it looked like a tiny lump of jelly.

Hydra drew itself up to its full height and made a bowing motion.

"Pleased to meet you, I'm sure," it spoke with a smooth, rather oily voice.

"I trust you are all well," it went on, "as indeed I am myself, except that this very morning some blundering trout bit off my head and I had to grow another."

"Goodness, do you mean to say you can grow another head!" Twinks was completely taken aback.

Hydra looked annoyed.

"Of course I can grow another head, and any other part of my body I like too. Do you mean to say that if *your* head was cut off you'd just go on without it?" The tiny creature positively bulged with scorn.

Here the River Keeper thought it best to interrupt, so he tactfully suggested that Hydra should show Bill and Twinks how he could turn somersaults.

"Certainly, sir, if you so desire it," replied Hydra somewhat mollified, and without more ado began to turn somersaults in the most amazing manner. Over

[211]

and over it went, balancing on its tentacles just like the acrobats that Bill had seen in last year's pantomime. Finally, with one tremendous turn, over it plopped into the water and disappeared!

"Hallo, River man," said someone near by in a gentle voice.

"Ah, good morning, Euglenia." The River man turned to a gentle, delicate creature, pale green in colour and with one remarkable bright red eye, and a long thread hanging from the top of its head.

"These are friends of mine, Euglenia," said the River man, turning to Twinks and Bill and Mr. Pobblethwaite. "When you see the green scum on the top of ponds and streams it is nearly always Euglenia and her family, and here"—he pointed to another round tubby little green creature that had popped up on the bank—"is Volvox, her cousin."

The two strange green things wriggled their jelly-like bodies.

"We're pleased to see you," they chanted together, "but we can't stop because we are going in for a beauty competition to-day and we have to go and make ourselves as fine as possible. Good-bye," and the two lashed their way into the water, their long threads darting from side to side like the oars of a boat.

"Now, my dears, we really must hurry." Mr. Pobblethwaite had taken out his watch again. "I promised to call on the roses before I went home, and time is flying."

"Oh, do wait a second," begged Bill and Twinks together. "Is it true that some fish live in mud and climb trees?"

The River Keeper held out his hand with a friendly smile. "Yes," he said, "but not here. I'll show you one day, just come along and see me at any time, I shall always be ready to tell you all I can. I'll give you a hint," and he whispered: "How do eels go home—I can't tell you now, but just remember that everything is living

[213]

and thinking and working, like you. Don't despise little things. They've all got a job to do. I've known a speck of dust start a huge rainstorm, and I'll tell you a secret— I once had a dog who was ill every time the air was cleaned."

This was too much for Twinks. "Good-bye," she said, "and thank you so much for showing us the river. Good-bye."

Bill and Twinks put out their hands but to their astonishment the River Keeper had vanished and instead of being beside the river they were standing in the King's Garden again in front of a rose bush.

The bush was a mass of beautiful pink blossoms. But what fascinated Twinks was the fact that the roses were busy at their toilet. Some were smoothing down their bright skirts with soft brushes. Others were powdering their golden hair with big powder puffs, and many of them were squirting scent over themselves out of crystal bottles. There was an air of activity about the whole bush as if some great event was expected.

"Getting ready for the bees to-day," said one to Mr. Pobblethwaite, as she arranged her shining locks with care.

"Splendid!" cried the Time Keeper. "You look more beautiful than ever, if I may say so, and younger too!"

"Go along with you, flatterer." The rose perked herself as if she enjoyed the compliment. "Oh, I hear them coming." She blushed an even deeper pink and began to tremble with excitement.

There sounded the low buzzing of bees across the garden, and as it grew louder five or six bumble bees came flying towards the rose bush.

They were fine, handsome fellows in their brown velvet suits, and as they came nearer the whole rose bush simply shook with anticipation.

"Good day to you, Mistress Rose." The leader of the bees, a magnificent insect with flashing eyes, dropped on to the stalk of one of the green leaves.

"Good morning to you, Sir Bumble," quavered the rose, spreading her bright gown. "I trust you are well, this beautiful day."

"Of all the beautiful things in the garden, Mistress Rose, you are the fairest," the bee gallantly replied, venturing to stroke the tips of the rose with his delicate wings.

"Oh, Sir Bumble." The lovely rose blushed even deeper pink. "You are a bold flatterer."

"Not so, wondrous Rose, for you are the lady of my heart," replied the bee, "and we have the whole summer's day to make love in. Let me sip the sweet nectar of your lips." And before the rose had time to say, No, bold Sir Bumble had put his arms around her golden curls and taken a kiss from her sweetness.

Twinks saw that all the other roses on

the bush were being wooed by eager bees, and the air was heavy with scent and the sound of the bees buzzing. She turned to Mr. Pobblethwaite and Bill who were watching too.

"I'm sorry for the roses," she said, "because to-morrow the bees will be making love to other flowers and the poor roses will be neglected."

"They don't worry about that, my dear," the Time Keeper told her. "The roses and the bees realize what their job is; they have a lot of happiness together and they know that when next summer comes round again there will be more roses and more bees and they will bud and bloom again. It's worth while to look neat and clean, you know, and flowers do their very best."

"How do flowers feed, Mr. Pobblethwaite?" This was from Bill who had been interestedly looking on at the wooing of the roses. "They must have some kind of food, surely, to keep them going?"

[217]

"I wondered whether you would ask me that." The Time Keeper stuck his umbrella in the ground and stepped a little nearer to the rose bush.

"It's the sun, you know," he said, speaking rather impressively. "The sun and the leaves together. I'll try and explain what happens. You remember how the oak tree got its food up from the ground through great pipes that spread to every part of the tree, well, the rose bush does much the same, and the leaves turn the water and nourishment taken in from the soil, added to something from the air itself, into food for the rest of the plant. But they must have the sun to help, the sun and the green stuff that colours the leaves too. It's just as if the plant prepared the mixture and then gets the sun to cook it. So all the time the roses are love-making with the bees, the rest of the plant is hard at work feeding them."

"That's marvellous," Bill said slowly.

[218]

"I'll never forget all the things that I've learned on this trip, will you, Twinks?"

"No, never," Twinks answered. "And I'll never think I can do anything clever either. It's made me feel that I've got heaps and heaps to learn."

At that moment Gardener Boffin came to them over the grass. He stopped and looked up at the sky, where faint grey clouds showed against the blue.

"I suppose you'll be moving on into autumn soon," he said. "I see the first signs of summer going now. I hope you young people have enjoyed the trip."

"Oh, yes, it's been lovely, and we've more still to see, haven't we, Mr. Pobble-thwaite?"

"Yes, so much that we simply *must* be on the move this very half tick; look!" and he turned quickly on his heel towards the other side of the garden.

Bill and Twinks turned, too, to see what he meant. . . .

Autumn

There was an old toad who said: "Thinking
Is very much safer than drinking,
So I spend the whole season,
Without rhyme or reason,
Just blinking, and winking *and* thinking!"

THEY were no longer in the garden. Mr.
Boffin had disappeared. They were standing in an enormous barn, lined with
shelves from top to ceiling, and delight-
fully cool after the hot sunshine.

"This is nature's storehouse," Mr. Pobblethwaite told them. "Here the flowers
and insects can meet and have a chat before finally going down underground to
sleep. It's a kind of half-way house and
store combined. Many creatures like to

DANCE OF THE BEETLES

Beetles dig things into the ground to make it sweet. They call each other to work by signals and jump for joy when it is nicely done

come here after their work is done to meet their old friends."

Out of the shadows of the store hopped a solemn-looking toad. It wore a pair of enormous goggles through which its bright eyes blinked, and it carried a wicker-work basket filled with nuts."

"This is Tomkins, the storekeeper," Mr. Pobblethwaite told them. "Tomkins knows everthing about everything and some more still, don't you, Tomkins?"

"That's right, Mr. Time Keeper. I've lived so long that I've forgotten most everything of what happened to me when I was a tadpole, but I'm right up to date with everything else."

"What do you keep here?" asked Twinks, who had been looking round her at the things on the shelves.

"Fruit and nuts for the birds and squirrels in the winter, and seeds and leaves and anything else that Mrs. Nature wants taken special care of. I look after rats and mice too—yes," he said, seeing everyone's surprise, "they're all important for something. Then I watch the paints for the autumn leaves and colours for the flowers' new spring frocks. Here comes somebody now after paint for the elm trees."

A cheeky-looking young man with an acorn cap pushed to the back of his head came up to Tomkins whistling and with his hands stuck in his pockets.

"Couple of pots of yellow paint, old chap," he said. Then, catching sight of Mr. Pobblethwaite, he pulled off his cap with a flourish.

"Ah, the Time Keeper," he said. "Hope you're well, sir, and that you've got plenty of time to spare, for we're that behindhand this season with the painting that the old tree is getting worried."

"Yes, my lad, plenty of time, for you, tell the elm that there's no need to fuss."

By this time the toad had pulled down two large pots of gold paint from a shelf and had handed them over.

"Tell the elm," said the toad, "that there's not many more left and you'll have to make 'em do. Now be off with you."

With another flourish of his cap the painter sped away and Tomkins turned to greet another customer who had just come in.

This was a dapper little pair of grey

squirrels in their smart fur coats and bushy tails. They were grumbling, both talking at once, at the lack of nuts for their winter store, and wanted Tomkins to promise them more than their fair share.

After they had gone out with a big load the toad turned to Twinks and said: "Them's the ones to grumble, they don't take no heed to put by any for theirselves, just steal the birds' eggs and eat the tree bark in the summer instead of putting by for hard times. Proper feckless, they be."

"Doesn't time pass slowly for you in the summertime?" asked Twinks. "I mean, when all the flowers and insects are busy out of doors?"

"Time pass slowly?" repeated the old toad. "Why, Missy, I don't reckon I think much about time. I just go on working hard and that's all there is to it. When I've given out all the stores that are wanted I just goes to sleep myself till I know it's time to set to work cleaning up the place again."

"How old are you?" questioned Bill, looking at Tompkins' nobbly rough skin and wise old eyes.

"How old? why, I don't rightly know that, but I expect I'm just as old as I am."

Here Mr. Pobblethwaite interposed.

"It's no good asking Tompkins his age, because no one knows it. But he was here so long ago that no one remembers when he first came."

At that moment there came a rumbling sound. Looking round, Twinks and Bill saw a spiny black caterpillar lumbering in at the doorway like a miniature tank.

It came right up to where they were standing and stopped just in front of Twinks.

"So you don't recognize me?" the creature said. "Just because I have changed my clothes, you don't know me. What a pity!"

"Who are you, please?"

Twinks certainly had never spoken to a caterpillar before, she felt sure.

[225]

Bill laughed. "I can guess who you are," he said. "You are the Red Admiral, only you've got out of your fine uniform now."

"Right you are," replied the caterpillar. "I am on my next stage now. Then I'll wrap my brown cloak round me and go to sleep underground again till the summer. I'm beginning to feel sleepy now," and he swallowed a big yawn.

"Fancy *you* being the Red Admiral." Twinks sounded regretful. "I do wish I could change myself like that all of a sudden."

"But you do, my dear, you do," said Mr. Pobblethwaite. "When you are grown up you are quite different to when you are a child. The real difference is that you take longer to do it than the Red Admiral."

Twinks looked puzzled. "Yes, I think I understand, it's the time business again that muddles me up so."

"I'm afraid I can't stop to talk," the caterpillar was saying. "I'm tired of keeping in step and I've got to go and see that Gaffer Mole has reserved my usual bunk for me underground."

"So long, you two, see you again in the summer," and off it lumbered out of the store.

Bill had something on his mind. He looked at the Time Keeper who was having a chat with Tomkins.

"Mr. Pobblethwaite," he ventured, "what's instinct? I've been taught about it at school, but I don't quite understand what it is. Is it instinct that makes all the insects and things do their work, or what is it?"

"You've asked me something, Bill, that no one has ever been able to answer properly. Some insects I talk to, say it is habit. That may fit in, and you and Twinks have habits from the past too, like the remains of tails, and the bits of fish gills. I think myself that it is a kind of inborn inspiration. Something to do with memory that they are born with. Not the same thing at all as using intelligence. I know very silly creatures that don't have any intelligence and whose instinct only causes them trouble. Perhaps it's just a *little* intelligence —'cause there's not room for much."

"What kind of creatures?" Bill asked.

"Well, I don't like to be unkind," continued the Time Keeper, "but there are the lemmings who live in Norway. Very silly animals they are. Rather like rats to look at, but not half so clever. Every so often the lemmings, in spite of being warned by me—and others—over and over again, get it into their heads that they must move. Sometimes it is because they are short of food, but more often it's just a sort of wish to travel. So they all set off in thousands and thousands and they go up hill and down dale for hundreds of miles. Of course the old ones die and the young ones get overtired, but they still go on and on till at last they come to the sea. You'd think they would have the sense to stop there but they don't. The stupid creatures blindly go into the water and swim madly till they all get drowned. I made a special journey to Norway one season to try to stop them when I heard they were preparing to move. They listened to me, and then went off just the same. Perhaps it's the moon." He shook his head sadly. "The moon does a lot of things to my time, we mustn't forget that."

"What a queer story," Twinks said. "But lots of insects are really intelligent, aren't they, Mr. Pobblethwaite?"

"Certainly, many insects think as a hobby," remarked the Time Keeper. "Bees, for instance. I've seen bees when they couldn't reach the honey of a flower in the ordinary way, bite a hole in the tube where the honey is kept and get it that way; and as for ants, well, ants are some of the most intelligent insects I know. They actually keep cows, ants do."

"Keep cows!" Twinks was taken aback. "What sort of cows, not really mooing ones, surely?"

"No, not cattle, but things called Aphides that are really green flies. But the ants look after them very well and get milk from them by stroking them! And I have seen a mosquito stop an ant when the mosquito was thirsty, and it gently stroked the ant till the ant, out of kindness, really gave the poor thirsty insect a drink. I know some other insects who dig houses in the ground and always choose a place where there is some root so that they can get water whenever they like."

While they had been talking Tomkins had been bustling about handing out stores to squirrels, and dormice, and many other woodland creatures. The shelves were nearly empty and the big storehouse was getting very dark and full of long shadows. The old toad came up to them. "I shall have to turn you out, Mr. P.," it said rather sadly. "It's getting near time to be putting up the shutters, and I expect you and your young folk will be wanting to go along too."

"Yes." Mr. Pobblethwaite began to walk towards the door. "We must hurry, for I must get back home in good time. Come, my dears." He hustled Twinks and Bill along as he spoke. "Good night, Tomkins, see you again soon."

And out they all three went into the garden again. . . .

Winter
Soon Again

Time can be either fast or slow
  For time is as you take it.
It's not the fact you've a watch that counts,
  But only what time you make it!

AT first they thought the trees were on
fire, for the colour of the leaves was so like
flame.

"They've been quick painting them,"
remarked Bill.

"Well, most of the colour is there all the
time under the green," Mr. Pobblethwaite
rejoined, "but it only begins to show when
the green has faded, and the paint from

NATURE'S STOREHOUSE

Nature stores up everything so that nothing is lost and so that, each year, Spring is better than ever because of the busy winter-time

Tomkins' store is only just dabbed on in places to make them a little brighter."

Although the brilliance of the trees made a glow over everything, the garden seemed different. Boffin had gone. According to Mr. Pobblethwaite he always went down to Gaffer Mole's to see that the bunks were ready for his precious flowers. And although the flowers were—many of them—still there, it seemed at first as if the gay, happy spirit of summer had gone. The rose bush had lost all its bright blossoms, and while she stood looking at it rather sadly, Twinks saw two dark shadows glide past, and as they went a breath in her ear said: "Good-bye, Twinks, dear, I've got my next buds ready, but I've *so* much to do before we meet next time."

A group of frogs went by croaking to each other about finding warm lodgings for the winter. Bill distinctly heard one say that there was some good thick mud at the edge of the pond, but they'd have to hurry if they wanted to book a place in time. In one dark corner a fat toad was grumbling that his grandfather had taken his usual hole and that he was badgered if he'd stand it much longer. All the creatures and plants were making ready to leave, the colour of the trees did not interest them much, all they knew was that it was time to go and sleep.

"My dears!" Mr. Pobblethwaite was standing by the wicket gate beckoning to them. "My dears, I think we have just time to see the spiders take off, and, if you would like to, I think I could persuade them to let you have a trial flight."

"My goodness!" Bill and Twinks were thrilled. To have a trial flight sounded just too marvellous for words.

Outside, where the gorse bushes and small larch trees were hung with silvery festoons of web, each one dew-starred and glimmering, they could see hundreds and hundreds of spiders making ready to ascend. It was a most extraordinary sight.

Each insect had a thin, grey cord attached to its body like the cord of a parachute, while the other end of the cord waved freely about in the air.

"Is it difficult, do you get giddy?" asked

Twinks of a young, intelligent-looking spider who was fastening the cord securely round its body.

"Difficult? Of course not. It's easy as pie," replied the spider. "Here,"—it produced two more cords from a pocket—"you two try them. All you have to do is to give a little jump when you see me go off and then away you'll sail into another country."

"May we go, Mr. Pobblethwaite?" asked Bill and Twinks. "And what about you?"

"You two have a try," replied the Time Keeper, "and I'll meet you in the wood when you land again."

The spider showed them just how to tie the cord round them so that it would not slip, and they found that although it looked so fragile it really felt as strong as steel. It was a lovely feeling to look up at the cord waving in the air and know that you were going to sail off on it to some exciting new place.

A gentle breeze began to blow and all the spiders began to make ready.

"Now," called out their guide, "I'm going up," and with a little jerk its silken cord floated off the gorse bush and away into the air.

Bill and Twinks grasped their cords firmly and gave a leap. Up they went and away they sailed across the meadow. They looked back at Mr. Pobblethwaite who was waving to them below. This was the greatest adventure of all, they thought.

Up and up they went. All round them were hundreds of spiders looking about at the unknown country-side. The air round about seemed filled with grey threads and grey-clad parachutists.

Twinks tried to control her cord and make it go the way she wanted, but it didn't seem to work very well and at length she had to be content to hold on like Bill and go where the breeze took her.

After a time they noticed that some of the spiders came down in other fields, or by the side of the river, till at last only a few remained in the air. They found that they were floating towards the little wood again, and after they had seen their first little friend wave good-bye from a big bush at the entrance to the wood, their own parachutes came gently down to rest in a little clearing where they found Mr. Pobblethwaite waiting for them.

"That was too exciting for words," they panted, slightly out of breath. "But how dark it is getting now!" added Twinks, and indeed in the wood it seemed as if it must be nearly evening.

The trees stood grey and sombre in the twilight. Most of the colour had gone now from their leaves and lay on the ground in heaps, the branches of the trees sticking bare and uncovered.

"Good night, little lady," murmured a deep voice behind them. And looking up, Twinks saw that they were standing again under the giant oak who had talked to them before.

with a swarthy face. In one hand he carried a stout ash stick and in the other a big iron key.

"I'm taking my two young people back home," Mr. Pobblethwaite answered. "I suppose that you are locking up now."

"Yes, I have to see that everything is as it should be; the trees keep a good watch, but they are tired after the summer work so that I must have a weather eye open myself."

"How lovely the toadstools are!" Twinks had picked up some brilliantly-coloured fungi from the roots of the oak and was looking at them delightedly.

"I expect they're all poisonous," declared Bill. "They look lovely but they are really bad to eat."

"Oh, no, you're wrong there," interrupted the Warden. That shows how little you mortals know about nature.

"Poisonous, indeed! A few of them may not agree with your dainty tummies, but most of them are very good, and, what is far better, some of them provide the most important medicines that human beings have ever used. You mustn't judge things just by what you see outside," went on the Warden. "The most tiny little moulds do some of the greatest and most difficult work of all."

Bill felt rather insignificant himself at the Warden's words and he was just thinking of an answer when a strange, flickering light began to dance in and out among the trees.

"Whatever is that?" The wood was beginning to get so dark that Twinks drew closer to Mr. Pobblethwaite.

"Will-o'-the-wisp, he's always about in the evening. He's full of gas too, that's what makes him shine."

"Gas," echoed Bill. "But I thought that gas came from coal; I didn't know that nature made any gas."

"Of course she does," rejoined the Time

Keeper. "Germs make gas, and in some of your big cities the gas made by germs provides enough for the whole of the people living there. And the bubbles you see in ponds is made by germ gas too. Nature has taught you humans a thing or two, because gas that lights itself is used to save sailors at sea."

"I never knew that before," said Bill. "I hope I don't forget all you've told us."

"I don't think I will," thought Bill to himself, "because I rather like winter now that I can live inside things too."

While they had been talking they noticed that the wood seemed full of shadows that darted about here and there. When Twinks asked the Warden what they were, he said that they were just plants hurrying off to get to Gaffer Mole's as quickly as they could.

The air grew colder and big drops of rain fell. Mr. Pobblethwaite buttoned up his coat and opened his umbrella.

"This time is up," he told them. "Come under my umbrella, shut your eyes and count ten."

Twinks and Bill did as they were told. The last thing they saw in the wood was the Warden locking the gate and a big white owl snuggling down in the arms of the oak tree. . . .

". . . Ten." . . . They both opened their eyes. They were back in Mr. Pobblethwaite's shop and the time was almost the same as when they first saw it, or five minutes earlier by *some* funny time.

"But we can't have done all those things in so short a time. It's impossible." Twinks was incredulous, and the Time Keeper smiled.

"You ought to know by now that time is your own to do as you please with," he laughed. "It *often* goes backwards in dreams and you've not been dreaming, have you? Well, I'll see you again one day, my dears. Now you must get along home."

But Twinks was determined to satisfy herself about Mr. Pobblethwaite's watch. "Please, please, Mr. P., do let me have a look at your wonderful watch before I go?"

The Time Keeper good-humouredly produced the great silver watch and held it up before her.

Twinks was amazed, for it only had hands, and no figures appeared on its smooth dial at all.

"But how do you know what time it is," she asked, "if it has no figures?"

"Oh, I just think hard and the time appears," replied Mr. Pobblethwaite. "You have a try."

Twinks looked hard at the watch. "What time is it?" she thought, and lo and behold there appeared the figures that showed the hands pointing exactly to 3.20 p.m.

Mr. Pobblethwaite smiled at her astonishment, and replaced the watch in his big pocket.

"Now off you go," he said, and before they had time to protest he had opened his shop door and pushed them both out, banging the shutters behind them.

The little shop vanished into thin air. They were standing on the same bank as before, the sun was shining and it was tea-time.

"Come on, Twinks, first to the right and we'll be home." Then he stopped. "We never gave back our spectacles." He put his hand to his eyes, so did Twinks. But the spectacles were no longer there.

"Anyhow, we have plenty of time," Twinks said, and from behind the bank came an echo, "There's always plenty of time." . . .

Conclusion

Of course, there can be no conclusion to a book about time and life. Time has no end. It is different all over the world and in the world too. So you, if you have read so far, will know as much about it as anyone. Because all that we can see of time is change.

Try to remember what happened fifty years ago, to ask someone to tell you. Ask what happened when there were no motor-cars or aeroplanes. When no one had heard broadcasting or seen a talking picture. Then remember that every cinematograph depends upon change and that, like everything else, it is just an example of time.

If you were to take a picture of a forest over several years and turn the handle in a few minutes, you would see creepers tearing trees to pieces and snails rushing along like racing cars. Magnify sounds too and you will be deafened by insects, rustling worms, seeds or buds bursting, and a scene so busy, winter or summer, that you would be alarmed until you speeded up your thoughts to match the pace.

Do not think you know all about Nature or about anything else. Do not forget that years ago people were very proud when they first made a wheel out of logs or when they lit a fire by using a drop of water as a burning glass by mistake. Realize that in a few more years we shall be the savages. For unless we are ready for change and unless we try not to be prejudiced, the world will laugh at us because we knew so little.

In this book *all* that you read is true.

"What!" you say, "can a light be made by stroking a cat?" Yes, it can. Not very much, but enough to make it true. Try it on a frosty night. Did you ever know before that everything on earth is alive or that you and the dining-room table are made of the same strange electric bricks arranged in different patterns?

It is true. Time changes the position of all these little bricks and so we change too with them. A house that has fallen down is still the same "stuff" arranged in a new way. This happens to butterflies and you can watch it. To you and me as well, but the pictures are more slow. So never let it worry you. Just look at it and say— "How exciting!"

Awfully nice to know that you are part of all these interesting things, that you have a share in the daisies, the bees, and the poor old worms that work so hard. You cannot be dull in a world where flies have their own "radio", or where pigeons fly home far better than you. Or where bubbles in ponds make homes for spiders. Or other bubbles make gas that can light up a whole city and make a will-o'-the-wisp on a summer night. Or even where you can imitate lightning by rubbing hot brown paper until it sparks to your finger.

Because all these fine things are useful. Everything you see is useful for something if only you knew enough to ask about its life. It is a good plan to ask. Good to be polite instead of thinking "It's only a rat". A rat can make a better tunnel than you could build without any help. You might be asleep almost for ever if worms did not irrigate the earth for you, and without sacred beetles all the dirt that seems to harm you could not be turned into nice fertilizer to make seeds change into flowers.

So thank things sometimes and when you go into a wood do not forget that it is other people's homes. Tread carefully and think about them instead of about yourself.

You are lucky not to have to work so hard as a worm, and if *your* senses are more complete do not forget that *they* can feel the bump of your clumsy feet far quicker than anyone else. So thank things often. It is very rude to use a telephone or to catch a bus without wondering how it works and how it came to serve you.

In the future we will not bother about things just because they are big. An atom or an orange is quite as good as a mountain. A flea is nearly as important as a dog, if you have the right kind of eyes. Nature makes small things as well as big. Nature is the child of time. We began our lives on the sea-shore in pieces so small that no one could see us very well, and its rhythm is still in our bodies as we breathe or dance. Nature is a great friend of time.

And if there are people in the stars they may think nothing of use because, perhaps, they do not need clumsy things like teeth and toenails. Perhaps they use heat to see with. Anyway, it would take so long to get there that you could be thousands of years old before you arrived. A blue-bottle in a railway train is like ourselves. It thinks that the carriage is its world. Do not make this mistake any more. Remember time flies, too, and that you have to be its companion for ever. Find out if you can about all you see and some things that you cannot see at all. Hurry up! What is good enough to-day is much too bad for to-morrow.

Why! . . . In a few years we shall have microscopes using light that trembles so fast that germs will be seen that were unknown before. We shall know about invisible cathode rays, about cosmic rays that come to us from other spaces. They may bring us health. Certainly we want to give them a welcome.

So who cares if it *is* winter? Everyone works just the same although you cannot always see them. They all march in time to the same band and are just as important as you. They think. Or they have instinct; who is to decide the difference! There was once a dog who collected pieces of sheep's wool from fences and hedges in his mouth. Then he walked into a pond with the tuft of wool in his mouth. All the fleas, for they lived on him like mistletoe on a tree, rushed into this wool.

Toby let go, drowned the fleas and walked out nice and clean. Of course he could not do that for a million years on end because of *his* time. But Nature can in *her* time. And then the fleas learn to swim; like sea plants that taught themselves to root in the earth. That, like everything else in this book, is quite true. Life is so clever that it should make us afraid to be sure. We should only think we *may* know and try to be sure by making friends with everything that lives with us.

It makes every day so much more complete if we are friends with things instead of patronizing them. I will confess that beetles do not wear hats or smoke pipes. But they have other more fascinating habits if we look hard enough. So until the day when we understand everything about those who share the world with us, I can fill up with human attributes in a beetle's-time-world and watch it speed up in the spring. Nature works overtime in the spring and just as hard at all seasons less easy to watch. Nor is it only beetles that sweep clean or worms that lay waterpipes. Snow ploughs up the ground very importantly. All the world is a vast workshop waiting for an inspection if you will imagine yourself dressed in another creature's clothes.

It makes us happier if we look out for "signals" from all the folk on earth we so rudely call "things". If only we had microscopic eyes and amplified ears we could travel in a different land. Yet it is there all the time; every bit of earth and hedge is buzzing with invisible life. The miracles of birds, plants, seeds, nature's adaptations from sea to land and even the spectrum of the sun are ready for you. Insects that build houses with nicely-fitting doors, others that build houses underground with old roots as wells. Fish that give electric shocks, streamline fish that used jet propulsion hundreds of thousands of years ago—these are all waiting to say good morning at various times in your day.

Some plants have a better sense of time than any human being. Most birds know their way home and remember their own doorstep in a way quite outside your ken. But remember that other creatures do not use your standards of light, size or time. These all form the pattern which you must spin in your heart so that it seems no more strange for a butterfly to live a few hours than for you to wake up when someone taps on your door in the knowledge that the long story you have been told in your dreams took just the time between that tap and your waking.

So it is with size. Someone once found that fish can read. But they discovered something even more wonderful. It is that there are things in the sea so small that a grain of sand in a house represents their proportion. Now fish knew that all along. Because if that grain is taken out we notice no difference, but the fish die if it is not put back.

Someone else found that if you dig up worms from the sand and take them hundreds of miles inland, they still remember to come up at the same time as the tides at their old home. Please remember to think of time and size and space without troubling about your own country where an atom might be an inhabited world. Please remember that we count no more in the chain of everlasting time than a germ or a daffodil. Then it is easy to make friends with the adventures of life. Best of all, remember that everything from a star to a carrot, a song or a beam of sunshine, is part of you. Part of your friend time who is always at your side. There is always plenty of time for anything good. Or as Mr. Pobblethwaite would say: "There are lots of times but only one lovely kind that is always right."

College of St. Mary of the Springs
Library

Books not reserved for any special use may be
taken out two weeks with the privilege of renewal.
A fine of 2 cents a day will be charged on overdue books.

GENERAL REFERENCE books must not be
removed from the library. SPECIAL RESERVE
books may be taken out over night after 9:00 P. M.
but must be returned before 8:30 A. M. the next
day. A fine of 3 cents Per first hour & 5 cents
each hour thereafter will be charged on overdue
reserve books.

 9-47